Michael Bond made ....
while serving in the Army in the Second World War.
In 1947 he returned to the BBC, where he had
worked previously, and spent some years there as a
cameraman. Paddington Bear was born after a
shopping trip on Christmas Eve when he spotted a
small, solitary bear in a large London store.
Paddington Bear is now a household name, and the
Paddington Bear books have been translated into
over twenty languages.

Monsieur Pamplemousse was Michael Bond's first
novel for adults. Such was the success of his inspired
blend of comedy, crime and cuisine that a whole
series of books followed, starring Pamplemousse and
Pommes Frites. *Monsieur Pamplemousse Stands
Firm* is the eighth novel in the series.

Monsieur Pamplemousse Stands Firm

Michael Bond

HEADLINE

First published in 1992
by HEADLINE BOOK PUBLISHING PLC

First published in paperback in 1992
by HEADLINE BOOK PUBLISHING PLC

10 9 8 7 6 5 4 3 2 1

ISBN 0 7472 3849 9

Printed and bound in Great Britain by
HarperCollins Manufacturing, Glasgow

HEADLINE BOOK PUBLISHING PLC
Headline House
79 Great Titchfield Street
London W1P 7FN

CONTENTS

1
OPERATION BALLPOINT

The scene would have appealed to Monet; and, given his eye for a pretty form and his unquenchable appetite for the good things in life, without doubt it would have inspired him to reach for the nearest palette and brushes with all possible speed, his beard quivering with barely suppressed excitement. It had all the ingredients for a masterpiece.

The occasion was the annual staff party given by Monsieur Henri Leclercq, Director of *Le Guide*, France's oldest and most respected gastronomic bible. The setting was his summer residence near Deauville; the date, 15 July. It was a date which marked the start of the Season; a season of international bridge, theatre, golf tournaments, jazz concerts at the casino, and above all as far as the Director was concerned, six weeks of horse racing.

The party was an event much looked forward to by the staff, not so much for the delights of Deauville itself – but because the Director was a generous host and they knew that the food and the wine would be beyond reproach; the surroundings and the ambience such as would have assured it a top rating of three toques in their own publication had it been eligible. In short, it was a chance for everyone to indulge themselves at someone else's expense.

The majority of the office staff had arrived in a specially chartered coach; by and large those who spent their days 'on the road' came by car as a matter of course; a few, like Monsieur and Madame Pamplemousse, had opted for the relative luxury of travelling by train.

The Director's summer residence was inland from the sea, in a wooded area halfway between Deauville and Pont l'Evêque; convenient both for the airport and the *autoroute* to Paris, which could be reached in under two hours. Nestling in a pocket in the hills, the house was scarcely visible from the winding country lane which provided the one artery connecting it with the outside world. It was a veritable paradise: an immaculately kept garden of Eden contained within a few hectares of land.

Any tourists, having visited the fourteenth-century Romanesque church in the nearby village, and still preoccupied by the sight of its ancient stained-glass windows and collection of canvases by Jean Restout, might easily have missed the house altogether as they went on their way, *en route*, perhaps, to one of the local cheese factories. But had they chanced to spy it through a gap in the hedge as they drove past, they could have been forgiven for assuming they had stumbled across a film company on location, or a freshly assembled kit of parts arranged for the benefit of a photographer working on the country issue of a glossy ideal home magazine.

The gravelled drive, entered via a pair of ornate, remotely controlled wrought-iron gates standing a little way back from the road, having wound its way down the hillside past weeping willows and a scattering of beech trees set in immaculately tonsured lawns, ended up as a large circular parking area outside a picturesque black and white half-timbered house of the sort normally encountered only in dreams or in house agents' advertisements found in out-of-date magazines in dentists' waiting-rooms. Bearing the inscription 'price on application', they had almost always 'only just been taken off the market' should anyone be bold enough to make further inquiries.

Between the house and an equally charming stable block of generous dimensions which served as a garage, there was a large patio dotted with garden furniture, the whiteness of which was offset by splashes of red from the mass of *Danse du Feu* roses climbing the wall behind.

As it made its way down the hill the drive passed a large brick and stone Norman dovecot to one side and on the other a stream with a white-painted wooden bridge which led nowhere, but looked as if it might. The stream, in turn, cascaded over a waterfall and into a large pond on the surface of which there floated a variety of ducks. (Guilot, who for some reason knew about ducks, had a theory they had been bought by the architect via a mail-order catalogue; they were almost too perfect a collection to have arrived where they were simply by chance.)

Perfectionist that he was, the only change Monet might have made would have been to divert the stream away from the pond in order to provide suitably tranquil conditions for his beloved water lilies. Although he was probably aware, more than most people, that even in Paradise, one cannot have everything.

Clad in a white apron to protect his green corduroy trousers and tweed jacket from the splashes of recalcitrant fat, and sporting a tall chef's toque on his head, the Director had been busy for most of the late morning and early afternoon dispensing hot *saucisses*, *andouilles* and *boudin noir* from an enormous barbecue in the centre of the patio.

Brushed with melted butter and served with caramelised slices of apple, the grilled *boudin* had been most popular

3

of all and he had been hard put to keep pace with the demand.

There had been pieces of leg of lamb on skewers too; *pré-salé* lamb from the sea-washed marshes of Mont St Michel.

The meal had started simply enough with freshly boiled shrimps – and for those whose preference ran towards a cold collation, to follow there had been a choice between lobster mayonnaise or thick slices of local ham baked in cider, accompanied by tomato salad and marinated cucumber, served with local bread and wedges of rich, yellow, Normandy butter.

There were those, and it has to be said they formed the majority, who were unable to make up their mind and found themselves accepting both offerings of the cold collation and then followed that with a selection from the griddle.

After a suitable gap there was Camembert, Livarot, and Pont l'Evêque cheese: all in a perfect state of ripeness – the Camembert, an unpasteurised version from a local farm; the Livarot, orange-coloured and served from its package of banded marsh grass; the Pont l'Evêque, soft and smooth in its golden rind.

And now, to complete the pastoral scene, a bevy of local girls, rosy-cheeked and dressed in traditional costume, appeared as if by magic carrying enormous earthenware platters, some piled high with freshly cooked *bourdelots* – apple dumplings wrapped in butter pastry – others with mounds of strawberries, and still more with bowls of thick cream the colour of ivory.

Cider – *bon bére*, the true Norman cider which remains still until poured, when it sparkles, frothless and pure as a mountain stream – had flowed freely throughout, although there was wine in variety available for those who preferred it to the fermented juice of the *pommes*. The Director was not one to stint his guests.

It had been a splendid feast. And now the after-effects were beginning to show. All available chairs on the patio were occupied, some clearly for the rest of the afternoon. Bernard was already fast asleep under a tree. Those who had gone so far as to bring tennis rackets, having mentally ear-marked the two courts at the rear of the house for an afternoon's sport, were having second thoughts. A half-hearted game of croquet was in progress. Glandier, never one to let an opportunity slip by, was chatting to one of the serving girls. Any moment now he would be asking her if she would like to see one of his conjuring tricks. Madame Grante, swaying slightly from a surfeit of cider, watched disapprovingly from a distance. Others were setting off up the drive to explore the village.

Monsieur Pamplemousse decided it was a good thing the usual group photograph had been taken before lunch.

He looked for Doucette, but she was some distance away, engaged in animated conversation with the Director's wife. Pommes Frites was busy clearing up behind the barbecue.

The Director, fresh from his ablutions, emerged from the kitchen, peered round the garden, then beckoned.

'I wonder if I might have a word with you, Aristide?'

As he followed his host into the house, Monsieur Pamplemousse couldn't help but reflect that it was a rhetorical question. He could hardly have declined, and certainly the Director hadn't left him any time to say 'no' even if he had wanted to.

He wondered idly what was in the wind. It struck him that his boss was wearing a slightly furtive air. His suspicion was confirmed a moment later when the Director, having led him into the drawing-room, excused himself for a moment while

5

he went off to make certain as he put it 'that they wouldn't be disturbed'.

Monsieur Pamplemousse glanced around the room. The works of several minor Impressionists adorned the walls, the balanced composition of antique furniture, silverware and other artefacts reflected the quiet good taste of its owners: taste which was not only quiet but expensive too, if he was any judge. Loudier, who had been with *Le Guide* longer than most, was undoubtedly right in his theory that the Director had married into money. It was hard not to feel a touch of envy; and he would have been less than honest if he had said otherwise.

On the other hand he couldn't picture living there himself. The Director moved easily in such surroundings. He was in his element. But had Monsieur Pamplemousse been asked which he would really prefer, his own or the Director's way of life, he knew in his heart which he would choose.

He crossed the room and looked out of the window. The rich pile of the Aubusson carpet beneath his feet felt as soft as had the freshly manicured lawn outside; a lawn which he noted was rapidly emptying of guests.

He caught sight of Doucette on the far side, still walking with the Director's wife, and he was about to open the French windows and call out when he heard a door open behind him.

The Director entered the room and as he came up behind Monsieur Pamplemousse and followed the direction of his gaze immediately withdrew into shadow, signalling his guest to do likewise.

'I suggested to Chantal that she take Madame Pamplemousse to see the dovecot,' he said, closing one of the curtains slightly. 'It should keep them busy for a while. The history of the Norman dovecot dates back to Roman times.'

Catching Monsieur Pamplemousse's eye, the Director made haste to justify his last remark.

'Please don't think for one moment that I wish to say something I would rather my wife didn't overhear . . .'

Monsieur Pamplemousse pricked up his ears still further. As an opening gambit the Director had assured himself of an audience. Guy de Maupassant could not have wished for a more riveting start to one of his stories.

'What of Madame Pamplemousse, *Monsieur*?' he inquired innocently. 'Would she be interested were I to repeat what you have to say?'

'You must answer that question yourself after I have told you, Pamplemousse,' said the Director crossly. 'I really cannot make these decisions for you. Speaking personally, I would err on the side of caution.'

Monsieur Pamplemousse glanced out of the window again, but Doucette and the Director's wife had already disappeared. Pommes Frites looked as though he was up to no good with the Director's Borzoi behind some nearby bushes. One of his senses having been satisfied, he appeared to be more than ready to round things off by assuaging a second. Monsieur Pamplemousse was on the point of wondering if he should mention it when the matter was decided for him.

'Pamplemousse, are you listening to me? I fear I do not have your undivided attention.' Clearly, the Director was in no mood to be diverted from whatever it was he had on his mind.

'I was about to say, Aristide, that we live in changing times. Only the other day I saw a young girl driving an *autobus* through the streets of Paris, and a very good job she was making of it, too.'

Monsieur Pamplemousse waited patiently. Clearly there was more to come. The Director would hardly have brought him indoors in order to discuss the merits or otherwise of female bus drivers.

'It is getting harder and harder to differentiate between the sexes.'

Monsieur Pamplemousse nodded his agreement. 'It is most apparent, *Monsieur*, in the area of *les toilettes*. I often have to study the pictures on the doors most carefully. Then, more often than not when you go inside you discover they are all one and the same anyway.'

The Director grunted impatiently. 'That is not quite what I meant, Pamplemousse.

'I meant that increasingly one finds women doing work which in the past has always been regarded as man's province.'

'Like coal mining, *Monsieur*?'

'No, Pamplemousse, I do not mean coal mining, although doubtless in some parts of the world – Russia, *par exemple*, it is already an established fact. I am thinking of nearer home.'

Monsieur Pamplemousse considered the matter. 'But we already have a good record in that respect, *Monsieur*. Old Rambaud on the gate was grumbling about it only the other day. Things have gone to the other extreme. According to him even the office cat is female. At a rough guess I would say the female staff in the offices of *Le Guide* already outweigh the males by some ten to one.'

'Ah, Pamplemousse,' the Director looked at him triumphantly, glad to have got his point over at last. 'In the offices that is so, but what of those on the road – the Inspectors? Is it not time we had a female Inspector?'

Monsieur Pamplemousse looked dubious. 'What of the others, *Monsieur*? How will they feel about it?' He couldn't picture Truffert taking kindly to the idea for a start. It was rumoured that he'd only become an Inspector in order to escape from his wife. *Le Guide* was one of the last bastions of male chauvinism – at least as far as the Inspectors were concerned. In many ways it was the nearest equivalent in France to an Englishman's club.

Crossing the room, the Director began nervously to rearrange some flowers in an enormous bowl standing on a table in front of the fireplace. 'For the time being, Aristide, there is no need for the others to know.'

'I fail to see the point, *Monsieur*. Surely they will have to be told sooner or later.'

'Not necessarily, Pamplemousse.'

'*Comment?*'

Flowers were rearranged yet again. The Director looked as though he was beginning to wish he hadn't started on them.

'That, Aristide, is where you come in.'

'I, *Monsieur*?'

'There is really no point in my telling the others, if at the end of her attachment the lady in question fails to make the grade. They will all have been upset for nothing.'

Monsieur Pamplemousse began to look even more dubious. 'But supposing, *Monsieur* . . . just supposing, she does make the grade . . . and there is no reason why she shouldn't. The number of women chefs in France is growing . . .' Despite his initial misgivings, he found himself warming to the thought of there being a female Inspector. It would certainly add a bit of sparkle to the annual group photograph.

'Why should she fail, *Monsieur*?'

'Because, Pamplemousse, at the end of her attachment you will make absolutely certain that she does.'

'I, *Monsieur*? Why me?'

The Director glared at him. 'I do wish you wouldn't keep saying "I, *Monsieur*?" It not only makes you sound like a

9

parrot, but one singularly bereft of a working vocabulary.

'I say *you*, Pamplemousse, because it is *you* to whom she will be attached – figuratively speaking, of course.'

Monsieur Pamplemousse stiffened and turned to leave. There was a point where lines had to be drawn and this was it. 'No, *Monsieur. Pardonnéz-moi . . . mais . . .*'

'*Asseyez-vous*, Aristide. *Asseyez-vous*, there's a good chap.'

Motioning Monsieur Pamplemousse towards a deep leather armchair, the Director reached for a decanter and poured a generous helping of golden brown liquid into a glass. It was dark with age.

'Try some of this. I am not normally much of a one for Calvados, but when in Normandy . . . It is a *Les "Aieux" L'Aigle Millésimé* 1947. I think you will like it.' He filled a second glass and downed it in a single swallow.

'I have a particular reason for asking. I know that in view of your past reputation I may be playing with fire, but I need someone of discretion . . . a man of the world. A man who will understand the problem and act accordingly.'

'I understand the problem, *Monsieur*. I can see the addition of a *femme* to what has always been a domain *masculin* will pose many problems, but as you said earlier, times change, and they need not be insurmountable. In any case, I have to say that to prejudge a poor innocent girl in this way would be grossly unfair.'

'Life is often grossly unfair, Pamplemousse. Life, for many people, is unfair from the moment they are born. As for the person concerned being "innocent" I doubt if she knows the meaning of the word. You might say that in many respects Elsie has little cause to feel hard done by, but when it comes to the allocation of "innocence" she may well feel she was given short measure.'

'Elsie?' repeated Monsieur Pamplemousse. A warning bell

began to sound in the deep recesses of his mind.

'Did you say her name is Elsie, *Monsieur*?'

The Director nodded unhappily.

'Not,' continued Monsieur Pamplemousse relentlessly, 'the same Elsie who for a brief period was in your employ? The English *au pair* who cooked *boeuf rôti* the night Doucette and I came to dinner? *Boeuf rôti* with a pudding known as Yorkshire?'

The Director looked even more ill at ease. He replenished his glass. 'You remember her?'

'I could hardly forget her, *Monsieur*. She cooked like a dream, but she was also the stuff that dreams are made of.'

'An unlikely, but devastating combination, eh, Aristide?'

'*Oui, Monsieur*. And I have to tell you straight away that the answer is *non*.'

To say that Monsieur Pamplemousse remembered Elsie was the understatement of the year. After their brief encounter he had lain awake for the rest of the week thinking of very little else. Freudian dreams involving Elsie had filled his sleep. Elsie dressed in the uniform of a water Inspector; Elsie dressed as a swimming Instructor; Elsie in oilskins rescuing him from drowning . . .

The Director took a precautionary look into the garden. When he next spoke it was with a lowered voice.

'Aristide, that girl is totally without scruples. Why she should suddenly evince a desire to become an Inspector heaven alone knows. But she is determined to get her way, and if she doesn't my life here will not bear thinking about . . .' With a wave of his hand which embraced that part of his estate which could be seen through the French windows he downed his second glass of Calvados.

'She is threatening you, *Monsieur*?'

'Not in so many words. She has simply intimated that if

there is a problem in granting her request perhaps she should visit me here so that we can discuss the matter in more detail. Can you picture it?

'You have no idea what life in a small village is like. Everyone knows everyone else's business. In Paris you can be anonymous. In the country, traffic through the kitchen is often worse than the Champs Elysées on a Friday evening. Then there is the Curé to be considered. *Monsieur le Curé* is one of the old school, steeped in the ways of a bygone age. The world with its changing mores and behaviour patterns has passed him by.'

The Director gave a shudder. 'I can hear the sound of her high heels on the cobblestones as she goes to see him.'

Monsieur Pamplemousse had a sudden thought. 'Could you not return to Paris for a few days, *Monsieur*? You could deal with the matter there.'

'And miss the start of the season? It is short enough as it is.'

'There must be other beaches, *Monsieur*. Le Touquet . . .'

The Director gave him a glassy stare. 'One does not come to Deauville in order to disport oneself on the beach, Pamplemousse.'

Although he didn't actually physically recoil at the idea, clearly he was distancing himself from it as far as he possibly could.

Monsieur Pamplemousse had spoken without thinking. On further consideration he doubted if the Director had ever been on a beach in his life. He certainly couldn't picture him with his trousers rolled up to the knees making sand-castles. Paddling as a form of pleasure would have by-passed him. Nor would he take kindly to Pommes Frites shaking himself over all and sundry after returning from a swim. He decided to change the subject.

'May I ask what happened with Elsie, *Monsieur*?'

'Nothing, Aristide. I swear on my copy of *Le Guide* that nothing untoward took place. What was intended merely as an encouraging pat while she went about her work, an avuncular gesture as she applied her feather duster to the chandelier in the hall, was grossly misconstrued. Or, to put it in another way, I suspect Elsie chose, for her own good reasons, to misconstrue it, filing the incident away in her mind for future use should the occasion demand. That occasion has arrived. Elsie wishes to be an Inspector.'

'But surely, *Monsieur*, if she brings the matter up, then it will simply be a matter of her word against yours.'

'Exactly, Pamplemousse. There, in your inimitable way, you have put your finger on the nub of the problem.'

Monsieur Pamplemousse fell silent.

'I have learned over the years, Aristide, that when it comes to a husband's word against that of another woman – whatever her age or circumstances or disposition, then it is the latter's word the wife invariably believes. When it involves a girl like Elsie, the dice are loaded from the very beginning. Nature has endowed her with qualities which give rise to immediate suspicion on the distaff side.'

Monsieur Pamplemousse couldn't help but be aware of a certain fellow feeling. 'But why me, *Monsieur*? Why not someone else? Bernard – or Glandier. Either of them would probably jump at the chance. Glandier especially.'

'Exactly, Aristide. And in so doing they would undoubtedly fall for Elsie hook line and sinker. Her little finger would be the least she would twist them around. They might even come up with a recommendation for her permanent employment. I agree that in normal circumstances pairing her with you would not be the happiest combination, but these are not normal circumstances.'

'What shall I tell my wife, *Monsieur*?' He couldn't picture

13

Doucette taking kindly to the news that he had a female attached to him, and if she ever discovered it was Elsie she would be down on him like a pile of bricks.

'Have no fear, Aristide, I have thought of that.' Sensing victory at last the Director reached for his wallet, opened it, and withdrew a somewhat dog-eared photograph. 'This is a picture of the daughter of a cousin of mine. As you can see she was not exactly in the front row when looks were given out. You can take it as an insurance policy. Should any enquiries be made *chez* Pamplemousse you can say this is your attachment.'

Monsieur Pamplemousse examined the picture. The Director was right. 'Barrels must have been scraped, *Monsieur*.'

'*Exactement*. If you must tell Madame Pamplemousse, then I suggest you choose a suitable moment and then arrange for her to come across the photograph by "accident". I'm sure I need hardly tell an old hand like yourself how to play your cards.'

While the Director was talking, Monsieur Pamplemousse took out his pen. The photograph was printed on matt paper and it was a simple matter to add a few spots in strategic places. In a matter of moments what had been merely unattractive became positively repellent. Trigaux in the art department would have been proud of him. He felt sorely tempted to add the beginnings of a moustache, but decided it might be overdoing things.

The Director rubbed his hands together briskly. 'Excellent, Pamplemousse. Excellent. You have missed your vocation.

'I can't tell you how relieved I am. I knew you wouldn't let me down. I must say that in some ways I envy you the task.'

Monsieur Pamplemousse brightened. 'You are welcome to

go in my place, *Monsieur*,' he said, clutching at straws. 'In fact, it might be a very good idea. Then no one can accuse you of partiality.'

'*Impossible*, Aristide. *Impossible!* It is the first of the season's important race meetings tomorrow. Elsie arrives at Bordeaux airport on the afternoon flight. You will need to be there by sixteen-thirty and as you know it is a long drive from Paris.'

'Bordeaux!' Monsieur Pamplemousse couldn't remember when he had last visited the west coast of France. 'It is a long time since I tasted the delights of Michel Guérard at Eugénie les Bains, *Monsieur*. They say he has gone from strength to strength.'

The Director gave a grunt. 'I am afraid, Pamplemousse, you will have to rely on the opinion of others for the time being. Les Prés d'Eugénie is not on your itinerary.'

Monsieur Pamplemousse tried to conceal his disappointment. 'Ah, perhaps *Monsieur* is thinking of Au Bon Coin at Mimizan. Mimizan itself is like an abandoned film set, but the lake beside which the restaurant stands is very beautiful and I am told that the small island which adjoins the hotel has now been laid out as a garden . . . as for the food . . .'

'No, Pamplemousse, I do not have Au Bon Coin in mind either. Or rather, Elsie does not. Her initial demands, I have to say, are surprisingly modest.

'She has expressed a desire to explore the coastal area around Arcachon. Quite why she wishes to go there I do not know, I suspect an ulterior motive, but who am I to deny her wish? It has the advantage of being relatively unspoiled.'

'It has the corresponding disadvantage, *Monsieur*, of being relatively unencumbered with restaurants of note. As I recall, Stock Pots are minimal.'

'All the more reason to go there, Pamplemousse. It will be a challenge for you; something to get your teeth into.'

It struck Monsieur Pamplemousse that in the circumstances the last phrase was singularly inappropriate. Offhand, he could think of many other places he would stand more chance of finding something worth while to sink his teeth into.

'Elsie has even given me the name of an hotel near Arcachon where she wishes to stay – the Hôtel des Dunes. Unfortunately it doesn't appear to be listed in our records, or in any other guide come to that, so I am unable to tell you much about it. However, accommodation has been arranged. You can use it as a base for a week while you explore the area. I told Elsie she could have that amount of time in which to prove herself and she seemed reasonably satisfied. The rest is in your hands.'

Recognising defeat, Monsieur Pamplemousse rose from his chair. 'I will do my best, *Monsieur*, insofar as my conscience will allow. I cannot guarantee the result, but in the meantime I will of course report back to you on a regular basis.'

'No, no! Pamplemousse.' The Director looked agitated. 'I have gone to great pains to make certain Chantal knows nothing whatsoever about my plans. As far as she is concerned Elsie went back to *la Grande Bretagne* for good. It must remain that way. Absolute secrecy is the order of the day.'

'But, *Monsieur* . . .'

The Director held up his hand. '*Discrétion absolue*, Pamplemousse!'

'I understand what you are saying, *Monsieur*, but supposing . . . just supposing something goes wrong. I may need to telephone for further instructions.'

'Things must not go wrong, Pamplemousse. As for telephoning me here, that is out of the question. It is quite within the bounds of possibility that either by accident or design Chantal could pick up an extension receiver and overhear our conversation, then where would I be? Her suspicions would be aroused on the instant.'

Monsieur Pamplemousse considered the matter for a moment or two. The Director was right in his last remark. He wouldn't normally have any reason for telephoning. The Director's wife would smell a rat straight away if she caught them talking.

'In that case, *Monsieur*,' he said, tapping his teeth with the pen, 'we must think up a reason. Perhaps I could leave something behind when we go today. Something precious . . .'

The Director clapped his hands together. 'Good thinking, Aristide. You have it right there in your hand!'

Monsieur Pamplemousse gave a start. 'But that is my favourite Cross pen, *Monsieur*. I shall be lost without it. Besides, it will be a bad omen I am sure.'

'Nonsense, Aristide. In a week's time you shall have it back. If all goes well you can have a dozen pens.'

Now that the idea had been suggested, the Director entered into the scheme of things with all his old enthusiasm. Without waiting for a reply he took the pen from Monsieur Pamplemousse and stuffed it down the side of the chair.

'No one will find it there unless they are looking specially.

'We must find a code-word. What is the English word for *stylo*? Ballpoint; we will call the whole thing Operation Ballpoint. Should you run into trouble all you need do is say the word and I shall be on the *qui-vive* immediately.'

Without further ado the Director picked up a small antique hand-bell. 'I will ring for some tea. No doubt you and your wife will be wanting to get back to Paris and have a reasonably early night in view of your journey tomorrow. After tea I will arrange for a car to take you to the train.'

17

* * *

'It's a lovely evening,' said Doucette, as they disembarked outside the *gare* in Deauville. 'Why don't we go for a walk and catch a later train?'

Monsieur Pamplemousse looked at his wife in surprise. It was a long time since she had suggested such a thing. Normally, she would have been only too anxious to get home.

Pommes Frites decided matters for them. Pommes Frites could smell the sea, and in Pommes Frites' opinion anyone who went to the sea-side and didn't go on the beach needed their head examined. Without further ado he set off in the general direction of the harbour.

The tide was in when they reached the yacht basin. On the Trouville side of the Touques estuary they could see boats of the fishing fleet being made ready for the night's work. In less than twelve hours' time they would be back again and the little fish market alongside the *quai* would be bustling with activity.

Monsieur Pamplemousse wished he'd thought to bring his camera with him. It was easy to see why the light had attracted the early Impressionists, although what they would have made of the hideous new high-rise apartments which blocked the view of the sea on the Deauville side was anybody's guess.

Crossing the little pedestrian walkway which spanned the harbour entrance gates, they skirted the port until they reached the Promenade des Planches – the boardwalk made famous in the film *Un Homme et une Femme*.

Pommes Frites galloped on ahead, blissfully unaware of notices reminding owners of dogs that anything untoward must happen below that area which would be covered by the incoming tide. It didn't leave him much room for manoeuvre.

'Aristide, is there anything going on between you and *Monsieur le Directeur*?'

Lost in his own thoughts, Monsieur Pamplemousse gave a start. 'Why do you ask, *chérie*?'

'Apparently he has been acting very strangely over the past few days. Besides, he made it perfectly obvious he wanted to get together with you on his own. Chantal knows even less about dovecots than I do.' The fact that Doucette was suddenly on Christian-name terms with the Director's wife did not escape Monsieur Pamplemousse.

'I gather it has to do with a letter which arrived from England, earlier in the week. Chantal found bits of it down the waste disposal the next morning. There was a picture of the queen on one of the stamps.'

Monsieur Pamplemousse gave his wife a side-long glance. 'What else did Madame Leclercq have to talk about?'

'Oh, this and that.'

They strolled along the boardwalk in silence for a while. A burst of screeching from a flock of sea-gulls wheeling in the sky above the harbour marked the passage of a fishing boat. Pommes Frites found a large stick on the sand and brought it for his master, wagging his tail in anticipation. Monsieur Pamplemousse absentmindedly obliged and had it returned to him in a flash.

'There have been phone calls,' said Doucette. 'And once, when Chantal pressed the re-dial button, she got an English number.'

'Did she find out who it was?'

'No. The person hung up immediately they heard her voice.'

Monsieur Pamplemousse breathed an inward sigh of relief.

Cars were starting to draw up outside the Casino, disgorging occupants in evening dress. From where they were walking he could see the lighted chandeliers within. The gaming-room itself would be closed to the outside world. There would be a room full of one-armed bandits of course – a sign of the times – but, apart from the cars and posters heralding a visit by Lionel Hampton and Dave Brubeck, he doubted if the scene was very different to the days when Marcel Proust used to go there regularly in order to gamble and dance the night away.

As they drew near, without either of them saying a word, they turned off the boardwalk and away from the sea.

'The fact is . . .' began Monsieur Pamplemousse, 'I have been entrusted with a very delicate mission. The Director told me in strictest confidence, but I know you won't say anything.'

As they headed back towards the town he gave Doucette a brief run-down of the Director's plans, omitting both Elsie's name and his own instructions; neither of which would go down well – it was hard to say which would be worse. Of the two, he infinitely preferred to argue his way out of the latter.

'If that's all there is, then if you ask me he's making a mountain out of a molehill. Anyway, I don't see why it has to be an English girl. There must be plenty of French girls more than capable of doing the job.'

Monsieur Pamplemousse gave a shrug as much as to say who am I to comment?

Halfway back to the station they stopped at a café. He suddenly felt unusually dry and in need of a long glass of something cold and thirst-quenching. He decided to stay with cider. Doucette chose a *citron pressé*.

When they had finished, Monsieur Pamplemousse called for *l'addition* and in opening his wallet, allowed the Director's photograph to fall on the table.

'It is so that I shall recognise her at the airport,' he said carelessly.

Doucette glanced at it. 'She doesn't look at all as one might expect. She looks in need of care and protection. Perhaps I should come with you for once?'

'Now, now, Couscous. You know how I feel about mixing work with pleasure.' It was hard to tell whether the question had been asked in innocence or not.

'Poor thing. Just look at her face. I've never seen so many spots.' Holding the photograph up to the light, Madame Pamplemousse subjected it to a closer inspection.

Monsieur Pamplemousse's heart missed a beat. Stamped across the back in large letters was the name of a well-known French processing company. But he needn't have worried. His wife had other things on her mind.

'How very strange.' She dipped her finger in a glass of water and applied it to the surface. 'Someone must have been defacing it. Look – the ink comes away. What can it mean?'

Monsieur Pamplemousse shifted uneasily in his seat. 'I think you have been married too long to an ex-detective, *chérie*. It has made you suspicious.'

'But don't you think it is strange?' Doucette wasn't to be diverted that easily. 'Why should anyone wish to do that? It isn't even well done.'

'I really don't know, Couscous,' said Monsieur Pamplemousse testily. 'People do the oddest things. I'm sure there is a simple explanation.

'All I know is it couldn't have been me.' He opened his jacket and pointed to the inside pocket. 'I have lost my pen. The one you gave me years ago. When we get to the *gare* I must telephone the Director in case I left it there.'

'Ah! That reminds me. I can save you the trouble.' Doucette reached for her handbag. 'I have some good news for you.

21

Chantal found it tucked away in the side of a chair. She gave it to me just before we left. You must have dropped it when you and the Director were having your chat. I told her how upset you would have been.'

Monsieur Pamplemousse was hardly listening; his mind was racing in different directions. Warning bells began to sound again, only much louder this time; a whole carillon. If Chantal had found his pen she must have been giving the room a fine going-over. And why had she given it to Doucette and not to him? It sounded distinctly fishy. It was imperative that he get in touch with the Director as soon as possible and warn him.

'Are you sure it is mine?'

'It has your initials on the side.'

They caught the 19.21 stopping train to Lisieux and changed there for the Paris express. It arrived at the Gare St Lazare at 22.01 precisely and they were home by half past ten.

While Doucette bustled about doing things in the kitchen, Monsieur Pamplemousse slipped into the bedroom. Keeping his fingers crossed in the hope that Doucette wouldn't catch him in the act, he dialled the Director's number. A problem shared was a problem halved.

'*Monsieur.*'

There was a pause. 'I am sorry.' The Director sounded sleepy. He must have gone to bed early, doubtless worn out by his exertions over a hot barbecue.

'I am afraid you have the wrong number. There is no one here of that name.' His voice had a muffled quality to it, as though he had his head under the bedclothes.

'Ballpoint, *Monsieur*!'

There was a certain vicarious pleasure to be derived from saying the word. The Director was right; it did have a much better ring to it than *stylo*.

For reasons he couldn't quite put his finger on, Monsieur Pamplemousse had an uneasy feeling in the back of his mind that he was about to be plunged into deep waters: waters that were not only deep, but black, with hidden undercurrents. As he replaced the receiver he took comfort in the knowledge that he was no longer the only one likely to lie awake that night wondering what the morrow would bring. A problem shared was a problem halved.

2
OMENS GALORE

Propping up the counter of Le Rendezvous bar at Mérignac airport, Monsieur Pamplemousse ordered his third Kir of the day. The first had been at an *autoroute café* south of Tours on the journey down from Paris, where they had stopped for lunch; the second when he arrived in Bordeaux, hot, tired and thirsty. It had hardly touched his lips. Now he was ready for the third, to be sipped in a more leisurely fashion while he kept a watchful eye on the exit doors leading from the Arrivals area.

It had been a long drive. Even using the *autoroute* all the way, it had taken over seven hours; eight if you included the stops. His *deux chevaux* was never designed to break the world speed record. Not, according to the barman, that there had been any great need to hurry; the summer schedules were in operation – the holiday season was about to begin – need one say more, *Monsieur*? As if that wasn't enough to contend with, there were the usual seasonal problems with Air Traffic Control.

Having poured the drink, he seemed pleased to have someone to talk to as he set about polishing the glasses.

Monsieur Pamplemousse listened with only half an ear. After being cooped up in the car for so long he needed time to unwind. Pommes Frites looked as though he was feeling the effects too; padding up and down the hall like a caged lion while he awaited his master's bidding, occasionally pricking up his ears as he caught the sound of an aircraft taking off or landing.

The Kir was better than expected, perhaps because he was in wine country. It was also unusually generous.

He eyed a row of telephones on a nearby wall, wondering if he should try ringing the Director. Then he remembered there was a race meeting in Deauville that day. Resisting the temptation to make a fictitious call so as to get a moment or two of peace, he inquired about the hotel.

'The Hôtel des Dunes? Funny you should ask that.' The barman gave one of the glasses an extra polish and then studied it as he held it up to the light. 'I hadn't even heard of it until the other day, and now you're the second person wanting to know where it is in less than a week. It's on the other side of Arcachon. Head for the town, then when you get to the other side, make for Pyla-sur-Mer and hug the coast road. Watch out for the sign – it's easy to miss.

'I'll tell you something else about it . . .'

But he had lost his audience. Seeing a flurry of activity further down the hall, Monsieur Pamplemousse downed the rest of his drink and made his way to join the welcoming throng at the bottom of a ramp leading from the Arrivals hall. He glanced up at a board as he went. It showed the AF1859 from London had landed five minutes ago.

Behind a glass partition passengers were already scurrying around looking for trolleys, stationing themselves optimistically in strategic positions alongside an empty carousel while they waited for something to happen.

A second carousel started up on the other side of the hall and everyone began moving again. It was like watching a television repeat of the opening scene in *Monsieur Hulot's Holiday*. Somehow people were always at their most vulnerable when travelling; sheeplike in their behaviour as they allowed themselves to be herded from pillar to post, anxious for reassurance and obeying every command which came from on high.

He caught sight of Elsie at the back of the hall. She was accompanied by an older man pushing an empty trolley. A moment later they disappeared from view. Elsie probably never went anywhere without people dancing attendance on her; a supply of willing hands ready to reach out and offer help at the slightest hint of a problem.

A few seasoned travellers carrying hand luggage emerged through customs. The first was an obvious Englishman wearing a tropical suit and a panama hat. Clutching a small leather attaché case and a pair of Bush and Meissener field-glasses, he disappeared with a purposeful stride; probably heading for one of the local bird sanctuaries.

Close on his heels came a sprinkling of businessmen; dark-suited, over-weight and perspiring slightly. He guessed they were in the wine trade on a late *en primeur* buying spree. Good reports were coming in about the previous year's vintage and some owners had been holding back in the hope of getting a better price.

Elsie was one of the last out. Her travelling companion had deserted her and she was making heavy weather of the trolley. Monsieur Pamplemousse's heart sank as the automatic doors parted and he caught sight of all the luggage. It looked as though she had come prepared for a long stay. If Elsie had aspirations to work for the *Le Guide* he would have to spell out lesson number one: never carry anything which wasn't entirely necessary. That would be yet another problem if they started employing female staff; a man could happily go on wearing the same suit day in day out. Elsie would have brought a different outfit for every meal.

Only too well aware of glances being cast in his direction, Monsieur Pamplemousse went forward to greet his protégée as she gathered speed coming down the ramp.

'Elsie! *Bonjour! Comment allez-vous?*'

'Oooh, am I glad to see you. I thought I was never going to get 'ere.' Elsie looked Monsieur Pamplemousse up and down as she skidded to a halt. 'You 'aven't changed much, I must say.'

'Neither have you.' Monsieur Pamplemousse essayed an attempt at gallantry. 'A little younger, perhaps.' He gave a sigh. 'Ah, how well I remember your Yorkshire puddings.'

'Saucebox!' A playful blow to the chest took him by surprise and sent him reeling.

Pommes Frites reacted with commendable speed. One moment Elsie was patting her blonde hair into place, the next moment she found herself pinned to a nearby pillar.

''Ere what's going on? What sort of a welcome is that? Go away! Shoo! You reek of garlic.'

'*Assieds-toi!*' Monsieur Pamplemousse leapt to her assistance. With ill-concealed reluctance Pommes Frites obeyed his master's command. Releasing his captive, he retreated a pace or two, at the same time keeping a watchful eye on Elsie's heaving bosoms: a self-appointed task in which he was obviously not alone.

'I trust you are not hurt?' Monsieur Pamplemousse also viewed her appendages with some concern.

'Nothing that a little bit of a rub in the right place won't put right,' said Elsie cheerfully. As she spoke she pulled back one shoulder of her dress, offering up an expanse of flesh for closer inspection.

'Can't see anything wrong with it, can you?'

Monsieur Pamplemousse shook his head. Patently the starboard *doudoune*, unencumbered by any man-made means of support, was as nature had intended it to be; large, firm and in pristine condition. He mopped his brow. Elsie's *balcons* were as he remembered them.

Out of the corner of his eye he saw the barman miss the top of a glass by several centimetres as he poured himself a drink.

'Allow me.' Reaching past Elsie he fed five francs into a *Péage* machine, waited for a ticket to emerge, then took charge of the trolley.

'Do not forget, *Monsieur. Embrassez le côte!* If you hug the coast you will have no trouble.'

Monsieur Pamplemousse treated the barman's aside as they passed his counter with the contempt it deserved. He led the way out of the hall and across a service road towards the car park.

His 2CV, still hot from the journey, had become hotter still through standing in the afternoon sun.

'Phew!' Elsie fanned herself with a magazine as she settled down in the front seat. 'It ain't half hot! I'm all of a fluster. What with your dog and everything.'

'Pommes Frites is very protective,' said Monsieur Pamplemousse as he climbed in beside her and started the engine. 'Also, I am afraid we had *saucisson à l'ail* on the journey down. It is made with pork, plus a little brandy and a touch of saltpetre. It was a local variation and it was unusually powerful. I think there may have been a little too much garlic.'

'You're telling me,' said Elsie, waving the magazine with renewed vigour. She winced as Pommes Frites breathed out heavily from the back seat.

Taking the hint, Monsieur Pamplemousse set about unrolling the roof canopy.

Once outside the airport he took the first right at a

roundabout on to a minor road, then right again on to the D106. As they settled down to a steady fifty k.p.h. he glanced across at Elsie. She was feeling around in the area above the windscreen.

'You will find a map in the door compartment.'

'Do *what*?'

Monsieur Pamplemousse tried rephrasing the remark. 'The map. It is in the compartment of the door.'

'I thought that's what you said.'

'I assumed you were wishing to navigate.'

'Navigate? I was looking for a mirror wunna I. A girl's got to think of her appearance. You never know. My mum always says that if you got yer make-up on and a pair of clean knickers it doesn't matter what 'appens to you. Don't tell me we're lost already?'

'I am not familiar with the area,' said Monsieur Pamplemousse. 'According to the barman we need to hug the coast. I think perhaps we should take a left soon.'

'Well,' said Elsie, with a note of finality, 'that's as may be, but for your information I don't drive, so I've not never 'ad to navigate.'

Monsieur Pamplemousse experienced a feeling of relief. The ability to drive a car was an essential requirement for anyone wishing to work as an Inspector for *Le Guide*. The Director would be pleased when he heard the news. If Elsie had to take driving lessons it could prolong the problem indefinitely.

'I was hoping that since you chose to stay at the Hôtel des Dunes you might know where it is.'

Elsie gave a hollow laugh. 'You'll be lucky. Some people say I don't know my left titty from my right titty.' She announced the fact with a touch of pride. 'But as I always say, if you follow your instincts who needs a map?'

Monsieur Pamplemousse concentrated on the road ahead

for a minute or two while he considered the last remark.

'Vanity mirrors are an optional extra,' he said at last, pleased with his command of the English language. It was not the kind of thing one would necessarily find in a phrase book. Most phrase books dealt only in negatives. 'This car has no vanity mirror.' 'The vanity mirror has fallen off.' The people who wrote them must lead extraordinarily unsatisfactory lives, forever losing their wallets or worse.

'Had I known that one day you would be a passenger I would certainly have asked for one,' he added.

Elsie pursed her lips as though about to utter the word 'saucebox' again, but had second thoughts. Pommes Frites was watching her every movement from the back seat.

'If there's no mirror,' she said, 'you'll just 'ave to take me as I am.'

'I am more than happy to, Elsie,' said Monsieur Pamplemousse. 'And please call me Aristide.'

It was Elsie's turn to look thoughtful as they drove along in silence for a while.

Monsieur Pamplemousse spent the time racking his brains as he tried to recall snippets of information culled from a brief reading of *Le Guide* during his stop on the way down.

It was hard to tell what Elsie was thinking. Her face registered very little in the way of emotion as she gazed out at the passing scene. It might have been a moonscape, albeit one which was dotted with signs advertising cherries for sale and peppered with little groups of cyclists limbering up for the coming season.

The fact that Sarah Bernhardt had spent the latter part of her life in nearby Andernos, riding around town in a little invalid cart after her leg was amputated, would probably leave Elsie unmoved.

He wondered if he should tell her about the time in 1927

when 80,000 metric tons of pit props had been exported by sea from Cap Ferret to *Grande Bretagne*, but he doubted his ability to strike the right note for someone who was patently neither a miner nor a wood merchant. He was right.

'Are you trying to make me wet myself with excitement or summock?' said Elsie, when he essayed an attempt.

Monsieur Pamplemousse decided to make one last effort. It was a case of nothing ventured, nothing gained. 'Did you know it was near here that a certain Monsieur Allègre built the first steam trawlers in the world? He called them *Le Turbot* and *La Sole*.'

'The trouble with you French,' said Elsie, 'is you bring sex into everything. I can't get on with all these "le's" and "la's". You don't know where you stand. I don't see no sense in it.'

'The French,' said Monsieur Pamplemousse defensively, 'are known for their logic.'

'Try telling that to a female turbot,' said Elsie.

Signs pointing towards the ornithological park at Le Teich passed without comment; the storks, the bluethroats, the bearded tits and the stilt birds could rest easy in their nests as far as Elsie was concerned; the mullet and the bream in the ponds and lakes were free to carry on catching flies with impunity; the ducks and geese would be able to continue their swimming undisturbed.

The nearer they got to their destination the quieter Elsie became. Monsieur Pamplemousse wondered if it was nerves. She didn't look the nervous type. If that were the case he was in for a fraught week.

On the other side of Arcachon Monsieur Pamplemousse followed the barman's instructions and took the coast road. Pyla-sur-Mer came and went and suddenly the whole of the basin was spread out before them. Away in the distance he could see a long line of white-capped rollers marking the point where the Atlantic ocean met calmer waters at the narrow entrance to the bay.

They passed some people having a picnic and he felt hunger pangs. Pommes Frites saw them too and peered out of the back window as they drove on.

The Dune du Pilat – the first and largest of the great dunes which formed a backdrop to the Côte d'Argent – loomed into view.

'"Pilat" means a "pile of sand",' said Monsieur Pamplemousse, as he executed a sharp turn to the left and the road began to wind uphill.

Elsie eyed the scene with a distinct lack of enthusiasm. 'They must be expecting to do a lot of building, that's all I can say.'

A moment later – just as the barman had said – they came across a sign for the hotel, half hidden behind some trees. If he hadn't been forewarned and consequently not had his wits about him he would have driven straight past. Braking sharply, he turned off the road. The driver of a car following behind gave a blast on his horn.

But Monsieur Pamplemousse had his own problems. Pressing even harder on the brake pedal, he skidded to a halt, just in time to avoid colliding with two police cars coming the other way. The occupants stared out at them. An officer in the passenger seat of the second car saluted Elsie. A colleague in the back passed a remark and the others laughed. The driver removed one hand from the wheel and gave the shaking of a limp wrist signal. There was renewed laughter.

Monsieur Pamplemousse could have written the dialogue.

He wondered briefly why there had been two cars. There were a dozen reasons for there being one; two carrying a total of eight officers suggested something more serious.

Moving off, he drove a short distance down a gravelled

lane lined on either side with pine trees. It was no wonder
the barman had been so emphatic. The hotel itself must
be completely hidden from the road. Monsieur Pamplemousse's heart sank as a building came into view. The
entrance to it was devoid of any recommendations whatsoever. There was not a single plaque to be seen; even the
Camping Club de France had failed to bestow any kind of
award.

Climbing out of the car, he automatically took stock of his
surroundings as he went round to open the other door for
Elsie. They were not auspicious. The obligatory menu pinned
to the inside of a glass case was hand-written and looked as
though it had been there for a very long time. From a distance
it was impossible to tell what colour the ink might have been
originally.

There was a sprinkling of cars with foreign number plates
parked to one side of the ill-kept driveway. One with English
number plates, a German registered Mercedes, a Renault 25
with a Paris number, a Peugeot with a Hertz label on the
inside of the windscreen, plus a couple of others which looked
as though they might belong to the hotel.

Pommes Frites jumped out through the roof of the car and
hurried round the back of the building on a tour of inspection.
He returned a moment or two later looking gloomy. Clearly
the smells from the kitchen area hadn't rung any gastronomic
bells as far as he was concerned; rather the reverse.

Entering the hotel, Monsieur Pamplemousse brightened
momentarily as he spotted a large fish tank just inside the
door. Anticipation was short-lived. The water looked murky,
and there was a dead *langouste* lying on the bottom.

There was no sign of a lift. The only area of wall where
one might have been was occupied by a large oil painting of a
woman on a horse. It looked as though it had recently been

cleaned, which was rather more than could be said for the rest of the room.

A pile of well-thumbed brochures spread out across a counter partly concealed a bellpush. They looked as though they might have been put there for that very purpose. He pushed them to one side and tried pressing the button. Somewhat to his surprise there was an answering ring from somewhere nearby.

An ageless person of saturnine appearance emerged through an opening behind the reception desk and eyed them without enthusiasm. Welcoming smiles were conspicuous by their absence.

'There are no rooms.' Bending down, he produced a COMPLET notice and placed it firmly on the counter.

Monsieur Pamplemousse felt in his pocket for a card.

'We have reservations,' he said firmly. 'Confirmed reservations for two rooms with bath. I do not wish to be difficult, but . . .'

With a decided show of ill grace the man consulted a list under the counter, then turned to a board behind him and removed two keys. 'Eleven and twenty-one. They are on different floors.' He seemed to derive a vicarious satisfaction at the thought.

'*Chiens* are twenty francs a night extra. Fifteen if you share.'

Monsieur Pamplemousse gained equal satisfaction as he returned one of the keys. 'You will find *Mademoiselle*'s baggage on the back seat of my car. There are six pieces.'

He turned away from the desk. 'If eleven is not to your liking, Elsie, let me know.'

Seeing that Elsie seemed preoccupied with the painting on the wall, Monsieur Pamplemousse repeated his remark.

'Eleven!' Elsie turned to face him. 'What do you mean, eleven? I'm supposed to be 'aving twenty-one. It was all arranged.'

Monsieur Pamplemousse took a deep breath. Initially his sole reason for letting Elsie have the room on the first floor was because there would be fewer stairs for her to climb. However, there was no accounting for the workings of the female mind, and if she was going to be difficult then so be it. Two could play at that game. There were moments in life when authority had to be established; parameters laid down. To his way of thinking this was one of them. If he didn't do it now he never would.

'I am afraid,' he said, 'I have already taken it.'

He decided to leave Elsie to it. She was well able to take care of herself. Already he could sense the other man was battling against his instincts over the matter of the luggage, and he knew which side would win. Elsie's pout at being thwarted had already been replaced by her 'little girl lost' look.

Signalling Pommes Frites to follow, Monsieur Pamplemousse made his way up the stairs. As he reached the first landing he came face to face with another picture. It had obviously replaced a larger painting at some time. A lighter patch on the wallpaper showed clearly where the previous one had hung. In the style of the Impressionists, the painting was of a canal in summer time. The poppies in the foreground contrasted strangely with a vase of dead flowers standing on a table further along the corridor.

Mounting a second flight of stairs he was aware of a familiar smell. It was a smell he had encountered many times in other small hotels: a mixture of heat, dust, and stale air.

His first impulse on entering his room was to fling open the window. He immediately wished he hadn't. Although there was only a slight breeze blowing, he could feel the sand stinging his face. Any view there might have been was almost entirely blocked by an enormous dune. It answered the question as to why everywhere felt so airless.

He closed the window and glanced around the room. Flowered paper covered the walls. The furniture was basic from a pre-war hotelier's catalogue. He ran his finger along the top of a chest of drawers. As he expected, it was covered with a layer of fine sand; it must have got everywhere during the previous winter's bad storms.

On the wall behind the bed there was yet another picture. This time it was in the style of an early Van Dyck. At least someone in the hotel must be making an effort. Whoever it was certainly had catholic tastes. The bedside light worked and there was also a telephone. The bed itself was firm to the touch and the linen looked crisp enough. In one corner there was the ubiquitous refrigerator with a list of its contents and the corresponding prices stuck to the outside. It must be a godsend after a day climbing about on the dunes. It was probably where the hotel got most of its profit as well.

The bathroom contained no surprises.

Monsieur Pamplemousse unpacked his bag, then looked at his watch. It was past six o'clock.

As he started to undress he fell to wondering what had made Elsie choose such an out-of-the-way hotel to begin her apprenticeship. Perhaps, despite her outward air of confidence, she was intimidated by large, glossy establishments, just as he had been when he was her age. Except that things were different now. Elsie's generation took everything in their stride, behaving as if the world owed them a living.

He wondered what she would make of the plumbing. Was she, even now, standing in the bath on the floor below him trying to operate the shower? If so, he hoped she was having better luck than he was. It took him a good five minutes of fiddling to fathom out the workings; another five to empty the bath, which in the meantime had become almost full to overflowing. The whole thing wasn't helped when in the middle of it all he heard someone trying his door handle. By the time he'd got out of the bath, wrapped himself in a dressing gown and reached the door, whoever it was had disappeared.

Monsieur Pamplemousse returned to the shower. Somewhere in France there must be a man with a grudge against society; a man who took enormous pleasure in designing bathroom fittings which effectively concealed their means of operation.

The occupants of the adjoining room seemed to be having similar problems. Snatches of German filtered through the wall; first a woman's voice raised in anger, then a man's. It was some minutes before the argument subsided, gradually merging with the sound of running water.

Although it was only a few minutes past seven when Monsieur Pamplemousse finally left his room, bathed, shaved, and wearing a change of clothing, the sun had already disappeared and the corridor was in semi-darkness. The dune must effectively advance lighting-up time in the hotel by a good hour or more.

As he fiddled with the key in the lock he felt rather than saw a momentary flash of light coming from somewhere behind him. For a split second he took it to be a flash of lightning. It was sultry enough for a thunderstorm. Then, as he reached the stairs and looked down, he saw Elsie disappearing towards her room. She was carrying a Polaroid camera.

Mentally Monsieur Pamplemousse awarded her bonus points. If she was already at work taking pictures of the inside of the hotel she must be serious about wanting to be an Inspector. It made up for her earlier behaviour. All entries in *Le Guide* were accompanied by a photograph. In the filing room back at Headquarters there was a whole library of references – several million of them – painstakingly built up over the years. He made a mental note to let Elsie have a go with his issue Leica. It might inspire her.

Monsieur Pamplemousse paused on his way down the stairs and took a longer look at the picture of the canal. Interestingly, someone had bothered to install a security alarm. Whoever it was had done a good job; the wire was barely perceptible to the naked eye. He couldn't help reflecting that if the picture was that special the owners might have chosen a better place to hang it; one where it would be possible to view it by something other than the light from a *minuterie*. Perhaps the simple explanation was that its predecessor had been stolen and the new one was simply a cheap replacement.

As he reached the entrance hall he glanced at the fish tank. The *langouste* was nowhere to be seen. An elderly battle-scarred lobster with bandaged claws had taken its place. It eyed him mournfully through the glass as though realising it might be next on the list.

For no good reason save that it was a matter of contrasts, it reminded Monsieur Pamplemousse of an incident which had occurred on the journey down from Paris. Returning to his car after lunching at an *autoroute* restaurant, he had encountered two men in white coats pushing a trolley. He'd naturally assumed they were delivering fresh supplies. It wasn't until he drew level with the trolley that he realised the truth. Lying beneath a sheet was a little old lady. Presumably she was being transported between two hospitals and didn't want to miss her *déjeuner*. She had smiled at him as they passed.

At the time he had found the brief episode immensely cheering; a sign of the indomitable spirit of human beings. Truly, a reversal of the saying that in the midst of life we are in death; a good omen in fact. Now, with the memory of the lobster fresh in his mind, its days clearly numbered, he wasn't quite so sure.

3
POMMES FRITES
SPRINGS A SURPRISE

On entering the dining-room Monsieur Pamplemousse found the atmosphere was, to say the least, morgue-like.

'*M'sieur' dame.*' Taking his seat at a table near the window he gave a courteous nod to an English couple and two young children sitting nearby. The wife pretended not to have noticed. The man was eyeing a *langouste* with disfavour. Monsieur Pamplemousse wondered if it was the one which was missing from the tank. Time would tell.

The woman glared at Pommes Frites as he took his place alongside Monsieur Pamplemousse. It was yet another example of popular misconceptions. The English were supposed to be fond of animals and yet they wouldn't dream of sharing a meal with their pets, preferring to leave them outside in their car and risk possible asphyxiation.

In the far corner of the room a group of three men were seated round a table poring over a map. From the way they were dressed and the cut of their clothes, he guessed they were Americans.

There was no sign of the German couple who'd had been having a row in the next room. Perhaps they were still making it up under the shower. He hoped the hot water lasted out.

In another corner a solitary diner – he guessed it might be a passing rep – sat turning the pages of a book in a desultory fashion. He had already consumed the contents of a bread basket and the best part of a bottle of red wine, and was no further advanced with his meal.

The rest of the diners looked as though they had been there for so long they were part of the furniture and fittings.

It struck him that apart from the English family, who had probably come down early because of the children, the one thing the guests all had in common was that none of them was eating.

He glanced around the room, automatically registering the decor. Wood-panelled walls – much too dark in the circumstances. More paintings. They looked as though they'd been hung without any rhyme or reason. Although having said that, he'd seen worse in many an art gallery. There was a still life near the door – a bowl of fruit alongside a vase of flowers – which particularly caught his eye and he longed to straighten it. The flowers certainly looked in better shape than the plastic ones on his table, which resembled no known species he had ever come across. He blew on them and a small cloud of fine sand rose into the air.

Unlike the bed linen, the table cloth felt soft to the touch. He suspected it had been there for some time. On the other hand – he picked up the salt cellar – the cruet was solid silver.

Monsieur Pamplemousse's musings were brought to an abrupt halt by the arrival of Elsie.

His own entrance had elicited no more than the usual covert glances and the kind of whispered remarks that any group of people make when they spy a stranger in their midst; their prior arrival having given them a certain proprietorial interest in the comings and goings of others who had yet to learn the ropes.

Elsie's appearance, however, produced a kind of stunned silence.

In marked contrast to the other guests, whose garb was not only casual, but in the case of the Americans verging on the *al fresco*, she was wearing a transparent off-the-shoulder evening dress which somehow managed to reveal far more than it concealed. Her progress across the room was punctuated by a series of '*Pardonnez-moi*'s', 'Please don't move,' and 'Oh, dear – silly me – I should have gone the other way – I do 'ope it comes off,' as she squeezed her way in and out of the tables.

In his role of waiter, the receptionist, revealing himself to be a man of many parts, followed closely behind, only darting on ahead at the last moment to ensure her seat was properly in place when she reached the table.

Menus and the wine list arrived with a flourish. Their order was taken; the wine – a Sancerre – arrived with embarrassing speed. Monsieur Pamplemousse tested it and nodded his approval. It had a characteristic 'gunflint' aroma and at least it was suitably chilled.

'Maurice is ever so nice really,' said Elsie, as the waiter departed. 'He helped me with the bath taps. I got in such a tizwaz with the shower, you wouldn't believe.'

Monsieur Pamplemousse surreptitiously felt below the tablecloth.

''Ere, what are you up to?' asked Elsie in a loud voice.

'I wish to make notes about the wine,' he whispered, reaching for his pen.

'That's your story,' said Elsie. 'Pull the other one – it's got bells on. I've met your sort before.'

'*Comment?*'

'Tell me what you're really up to.'

'I have a secret compartment in my right trouser leg,'

hissed Monsieur Pamplemousse. 'It is where I keep my notebook.'

'If I get a job as an Inspector,' said Elsie, 'I could keep a notebook up my knickers. 'Cept I don't always wear any and even if I did it might fall out, if you know what I mean.'

Monsieur Pamplemousse was conscious of a lull in the conversation around him. The English family were staring in his direction; the man twirled his moustache thoughtfully as he eyed the back of Elsie's dress. His wife was telling the children to eat up and not ask questions.

The smaller of the two asked why not. The mother asked why it kept on asking questions. The child asked why she wanted to know.

It was a no-win situation for the mother.

He caught the word 'disgusting' as a platter of oysters resting on a bed of fresh ice and seaweed arrived at their table. He wasn't sure whether it applied to the food, to him personally, or the hotel in general.

'One of the chief rules an Inspector working for *Le Guide* has to obey,' said Monsieur Pamplemousse, 'is that of anonymity. Total and absolute anonymity.'

'What, no free meals?' exclaimed Elsie.

'No free meals,' said Monsieur Pamplemousse firmly, 'on pain of instant dismissal.' He made an entry in his notebook.

'What you writing?'

'I was making a comment on the *huîtres*. I think seven out of ten for presentation, don't you agree?'

Elsie helped herself to one. 'I'll tell you something for nothing. I wouldn't give them much for "you know what". Anyone what was expecting them to do the trick would 'ave another think coming. I don't feel a bit randy, do you?'

Monsieur Pamplemousse couldn't help but be aware that the rest of the dining-room was hanging on his answer. Even

Pommes Frites looked interested.

'They are not at their best at this time of the year,' he said. 'It is the breeding season and they have a certain milkiness.'

'They're no more *fines de claires* than what I am,' continued Elsie, warming to her subject. 'I bet if they 'ad a "sell by" date stamped on their shells you wouldn't be eating them. I only 'ope they didn't come out of the same tank as that dead *langouste*.'

Out of the corner of his eye, Monsieur Pamplemousse saw the man at the next table stiffen, his fork poised halfway to his mouth.

'To give them the benefit of the doubt,' he said, 'they are old enough and large enough to be called *huîtres raptures*. They would have been better roasted and served with a little garlic butter and lots of bread.'

'My mum', said Elsie, 'used to simmer them in their own juice, wrap them in bacon, grill them, then serve them on toast – 'Angels on Horseback'.

'Funny things, oysters,' she continued dreamily. 'I wonder what it's like changing sex every now and again?'

'Confusing, I would imagine,' said Monsieur Pamplemousse.

'It wouldn't 'alf give some people a shock if you picked the right moment to do it.'

They sat in silence for a while, each busy with their own thoughts. Monsieur Pamplemousse found it hard to picture Elsie as being anything other than what she was, although from some of the tales he'd heard from Loudier about the nightly goings on in the Bois de Boulogne anything was possible. Loudier was near to retirement and did the Paris area.

'You have oysters in *Angleterre* then?' he remarked politely as the waiter removed the dish. 'I thought you mostly ate fish and chips wrapped in newspaper.'

'Do we ever. Mind you, it's not like it was. According to

my old dad, Royal Whitstable natives bred on London clay
used to be the best in the world. Where I was brought up there
was whelks and cockles and mussels every Saturday evening
as well. I used to eat them out of a paper bag on the way 'ome
from the flicks.' Elsie was clearly her old self again. Her
enthusiasm was infectious, and Monsieur Pamplemousse found
himself discoursing on the many and varied habits of crusta-
cea, large and small.

While they were talking the waiter arrived with their second course. Monsieur Pamplemousse gazed at the plate as it
was put before him.

'The annual consumption of oysters in France is over eighty
thousand tons,' he continued.

'I expect that accounts for a lot of things,' said Elsie darkly.
She paused and looked across the table at him. 'Is everything
all right?'

'*Non!*' Monsieur Pamplemousse glared down at his plate.
'*Non.* It is far from all right.'

He signalled for the waiter. Since they were by the sea it
had seemed a good idea to choose *turbot sauce messine*. Dreams
of a freshly caught turbot reposing in a dish of milk and water
whilst being baked in a slow oven, then served with a sauce
made from melted butter and flour, eggs, cream and mustard, gently stirred the while as leaves from a sprig or two
of tarragon, parsley, chervil and chives were added, disappeared.

He prodded the contents of the dish with a knife. A smell
of stale fish filled the air. The flesh didn't simply come away
from the bone, it positively fell off as though it couldn't wait
to escape. Pommes Frites took one look at it and then made
for the exit.

'I see what you mean,' said Elsie. 'I could do better than
that with one 'and tied behind my back.'

Monsieur Pamplemousse braced himself as the waiter drew near. 'Will you kindly return this dish to the kitchen,' he exclaimed. 'Pay my respects to the chef and tell him it is so grossly over-cooked even its own mother wouldn't recognise it.'

'And while you're at it you can tell 'im the plate's colder than an Eskimo's bum,' added Elsie.

'I am afraid that will not be possible,' said the waiter.

'Not possible?' Monsieur Pamplemousse felt his hackles begin to rise. Once again he reached for his pen – this time in deadly earnest.

'The *patron* has disappeared. He went out two days ago to buy some cigarettes and he hasn't been seen since. Madame Bouet has taken to her bed. And as Monsieur Bouet is also the chef . . .'

'I am sorry to hear that,' Monsieur Pamplemousse looked slightly less aggrieved. 'But what about the *brigade*? Can they not take over?'

The waiter raised his eyes to heaven. 'There is no *brigade*, *Monsieur*. There is only old Pierre. He is doing his best, but in the twenty-five years he has been here he has never once been allowed near the stove.'

'He wasn't joking when he said they 'ad problems,' said Elsie as the man disappeared again. 'I'll tell you something else. There's someone got their eyes on you. They keep giving you funny looks.'

Monsieur Pamplemousse grunted. He felt like saying that ever since Elsie entered the room people had been giving him funny looks. If the rest of the diners had anything else in common, other than a lack of food, it was they were all taking an inordinate interest in everything he said or did and he was suddenly filled with an overwhelming desire to escape.

'Shall we take *café* elsewhere?'

'What and miss the sweet trolley?'

'Another very good reason,' said Monsieur Pamplemousse. It wasn't always easy to tell whether or not Elsie was being serious.

Elsewhere resolved itself into a small room which was clearly reserved for breakfast. There were six tables covered with red and white checked cloths. The walls were lined with matchboard, painted brown, and there was an old dresser which seemed to be a repository for a collection of equally ancient magazines. On one of the walls there was a painting of a beach scene. At least it was an improvement on the dining-room where, apart from the still-life, most of the pictures had been of an ecclesiastical nature.

Elsie picked up one of a pair of bronze figures on a shelf and turned it over.

'You like them?' asked Monsieur Pamplemousse.

'You don't 'ave to like them,' said Elsie. 'They're by Jaquet.' Without waiting for an answer, if indeed there was one, she picked up a pack of cards.

'Know any tricks to pass the time?'

Monsieur Pamplemousse thought for a moment. 'There is *Cherchez la femme*. If you like I will show you.'

Removing the ace of spades, the ace of diamonds and the queen of hearts from the pack, he laid them face downwards in a row on one of the tables, making sure the queen was in the middle.

'Tell me where the queen is.'

'It looks a bit like what we call "Find the Lady",' said Elsie, pointing to one of the outside cards.

'Oh, Glandier, where are you now?' thought Monsieur Pamplemousse, as he turned it over to reveal one of the aces. By sheer coincidence he'd watched his colleague demonstrate the three-card trick at the Director's party and the mechanics of it were still fresh in his mind.

'Shall we try again?' he asked. 'This time, I want you to watch my hands very carefully.'

Picking up an ace with his left hand, he showed it to Elsie, then he gathered up the other two cards with his right hand, making sure that she could see the queen was underneath the second ace.

Slowly and carefully he laid the cards face down again, placing the queen on his right.

'I think it's that one,' said Elsie, pointing to the middle card.

'*Non*.' Monsieur Pamplemousse tried hard to keep the note of irritation from his voice. The whole object of the preliminary exercise was to make the punter feel over-confident. He could hardly do that if Elsie kept getting it wrong.

'Ooh, you are clever,' said Elsie, after she had failed to get it right for the fifth time running. 'Can we do it properly now? Like me putting a little something on it?'

Monsieur Pamplemousse shook his head. 'I would not dream of taking your money.'

'Oh, go on – be a sport.' Elsie touched his jacket lapel lightly with her hand. 'Let's 'ave a bit of fun.'

Faced with Elsie's round blue eyes gazing imploring into his, Monsieur Pamplemousse felt himself weakening.

'If you really wish to . . .'

'Yes, please,' said Elsie. She looked round. 'Oh, dear. Silly me! I've left my bag upstairs. Would you mind lending me a hundred francs?'

'A hundred?'

'It's not worth playing for matchsticks,' said Elsie.

Monsieur Pamplemousse hesitated, then reached for his wallet. 'On one condition . . .' Despite Glandier's theory that

49

there was one born every minute so why not make good use of the fact, it hardly seemed right to take advantage of such childlike innocence. 'If you win you may keep it. If you lose then you need only give me my hundred francs back.'

'Sounds fair enough,' said Elsie.

Monsieur Pamplemousse went through his routine again, picking up one of the aces with his left hand, gathering up the queen and the other ace with his right. This time when he threw the cards on to the table he arranged for the queen to end up on his left. It hardly seemed worth bothering with the subtlety of relying on quickness of the hand to deceive the eye and dealing the top rather than the bottom card first.

'I think it's that one,' said Elsie, pointing to the card on his left.

'I bet you thought I was going to choose the one in the middle,' she said cheerfully. 'Oh dear, now I've been and gone and taken your money.'

Monsieur Pamplemousse watched his note disappear into the dark recesses of Elsie's cleavage. He resolved to ring Glandier in the morning.

'You could try winning it back,' said Elsie. 'I think I'm getting the hang of it now.'

'I think,' said Monsieur Pamplemousse, 'I may take Pommes Frites for a walk.'

He was about to leave the hotel when he heard his name being called.

'Monsieur Pamplemousse. Monsieur Pamplemousse. *Le téléphone.*'

Monsieur Pamplemousse hesitated, then signalled Pommes Frites to go on ahead. 'I will take it in my room.' He had a feeling in the back of his mind that it might be the Director; a feeling that was confirmed a few minutes later when, breathing heavily from having taken the last few stairs at the double, he picked up his bedside receiver.

'Pamplemousse!' The Director sounded equally short of breath. 'Where on earth have you been?'

'I am sorry, *Monsieur*. I came as quickly as I could. Is anything the matter? Are you all right?'

'No, I am not all right.' There was a muffled bark from the other end of the line. 'I cannot keep my head under the bed-clothes for very much longer.'

Monsieur Pamplemousse looked at his watch. It was barely twenty-thirty. '*Monsieur* is in bed?'

'Pamplemousse, I would hardly have my head under the bedclothes were I sitting outside on the lawn.'

Monsieur Pamplemousse stood rebuked. 'No, *Monsieur*, but . . .'

'I am in bed,' continued the Director, obviously choosing his words with care, 'because I am extremely tired. And before you ask me why I am extremely tired, I will tell you.

'I received your message last night, Pamplemousse. It came through loud and clear, despite my having to hold the receiver under the duvet.'

'I trust it did not cause you problems, *Monsieur*.'

'It might have done, had it not been for the fact that on the spur of the moment I made up a story about an itinerant *plume* salesman. One has to think on one's feet, Pamplemousse.'

'Or even lying down, *Monsieur*.'

The Director ignored the remark. 'Unfortunately, Chantal chose not to believe me. She has, I fear, a suspicious nature. She spent practically the whole of the night questioning me. As fast as I nodded off she woke me again. Today has been even worse. She hasn't let me get anywhere near a telephone.'

'Women, *Monsieur*.' Monsieur Pamplemousse sometimes envied the Director's happy knack of convincing himself of the veracity of his own stories. He couldn't help but wonder if

51

he would have felt even more outraged had he been telling the truth.

'I trust you have settled in, Aristide?' The Director sounded slightly mollified. 'I did ask that you be given a good room – one facing *la mer*. Elsie, I understand, had already stated her preference.'

'Without consulting a compass, *Monsieur*, it is hard to tell whether my room is facing the sea or not. The highest sand dune in Europe happens to be standing immediately outside my window. The only point in its favour is that at least I am protected from the worst of the elements. Although, having said that, it is the only hotel I have stayed in where it is necessary to empty the sand out of one's shoes *before* going on to the beach.'

'Not worth a detour, Aristide?'

'Even if one happened to be within a hundred metres, *Monsieur*, it would not be worth making a detour.'

'How strange. Elsie was most adamant that she wished to stay there. By the way, how is Elsie?' Monsieur Pamplemousse thought he detected a note of nervousness in the Director's voice.

'Earlier this evening she was talking of changing her sex. Apart from that she is well.'

'That shows remarkable dedication. Would there were more in our organisation prepared to make such a sacrifice.'

'I do not think it had anything to do with her wish to be an Inspector, *Monsieur*.'

'Nothing you have done, Pamplemousse, I trust?' said the Director anxiously.

'Certainly not, *Monsieur*.'

'Irrespective of the surgical problems involved – and in Elsie's case I would say they are considerable – it would not be good news. An added complication . . .'

'You were about to say, *Monsieur* . . .' Monsieur Pamplemousse broke in quickly before the Director indulged in yet another flight of fancy.

'Ah, yes, thank you for reminding me, Aristide. Chantal will be back from the bathroom at any moment. I grant you she spends an inordinate amount of time in there – what she does I have no idea, but there are limits to the amount of time even she can spend in front of a mirror – I rang to warn you . . . Don't, on any account . . .'

Whatever else the Director had been about to say was lost in a rustle of bedclothes. His voice suddenly came through loud and clear.

'Good. Good. It was kind of you to ring. In that case I will order six kilos of *framboises* . . . If you have any problems, let me know at once. Make sure they are in perfect condition. We have important guests . . .'

Monsieur Pamplemousse replaced the receiver. The Director had obviously added an itinerant raspberry-seller to his list of callers. It was to be hoped it would meet with more success than his previous effort. If it didn't he could be in for another sleepless night.

Sitting on the edge of his bed mulling over the conversation, Monsieur Pamplemousse wondered what on earth it was he mustn't do. He was so lost in thought it was a moment or two before he realised someone was knocking on his door. It sounded urgent.

He opened the door and Elsie entered clutching her Polaroid camera.

''Ere, you know your dog . . .'

'Pommes Frites? Of course I know him. Why do you ask?'

'Because he's just gone past my window and 'e 'ad a whatjemecallit in his mouth . . . You know, a *jambon*.'

'A *jambon*? But I doubt if there is a *boucherie* within

several kilometres of here.' Monsieur Pamplemousse considered the other possibilities. 'Unless, of course, he has discovered an out-of-town *Super-Marché*.'

'It wasn't,' said Elsie meaningly, 'the kind of *jambon* you'd find in a supermarket – not even a French one.' She handed him a print. 'Just you wait till you see what's on that.'

4
ENCORE

Monsieur Pamplemousse took the print from Elsie and held it up to the light. The faint image he'd spotted when she first entered his room was already forming itself into a picture.

'*Sacré bleu!*' He saw what she meant. It was a good likeness of Pommes Frites. Although he wasn't actually smiling at the lens, the camera had caught a certain self-satisfied expression on his face as it recorded him hurrying past some bushes outside the hotel. Fresh details were emerging with every passing moment. Traces of yellow sand were clearly visible on the end of his nose; the colour of his coat – the rich blacks, the reddish tints and the fawns – were all there, along with the green of the foliage in the background. It was a tribute to Dr Edwin Land's invention which, making use of a sandwich of chemicals and a couple of rollers, enabled a photograph to manifest itself before one's very eyes in a matter of moments.

All the same, it was not the kind of picture even one of Pommes Frites' most ardent admirers would have singled out for pasting in the family album. Still less would they have awarded it a place of honour on the mantelpiece, and Monsieur Pamplemousse gave the principal subject hardly more than a passing glance. He concentrated instead on the object

Pommes Frites was carrying. In particular his attention was directed towards an ominous red trickle which disappeared out of the bottom left corner of the picture.

There was no denying that Elsie was correct in identifying the object as a *jambon*, but it was a judgement which would have won her no prizes in a photographic competition; tickets for a holiday for two in the Algarve would not have come winging her way. Even the rawest recruit to the world of *boucherie*, an apprentice butcher learning his trade or a sausage-maker fresh from a school of *charcuterie*, would have had little difficulty in deducing the fact that whatever its origins, the *jambon* in question had never been an integral part of either beast or fowl; comparisons with wall charts would have been a waste of the instructor's time.

Any lingering doubts as to possible alternatives would have been instantly dispelled by the fact that a good four-fifths of the object was covered, not in caterer's muslin, but in the tattered remains of some thicker, white material, from the far end of which there protruded a foot. A foot which, in turn, was encased in an old-fashioned wooden *sabot* of the kind favoured by some older members of the catering trade whose work entailed their spending long hours slaving over a hot stove.

It was no wonder Pommes Frites was looking pleased with himself. Had he still been a member of the élite *Division Chiens* of the Paris Sûreté he might well have been in line for a commendation.

'Queer, innit,' said Elsie soberly. 'Gave me quite a shock when I saw 'im go past with it sticking out of 'is mouth.'

'We must find him immediately.' Removing a flashlight from his bag, Monsieur Pamplemousse reached for the door handle. He had a sudden mental picture of Pommes Frites entering the hotel and running round the dining-room, anxious to show off his prize to all and sundry. It didn't bear thinking about. An even worse possibility was if he happened to bump into Madame Bouet, freshly risen from her bed. It might send her back there, never to rise again.

Although the evidence was purely circumstantial, the conclusion that the object in Pommes Frites' mouth had once belonged to the missing *patron* of the Hôtel des Dunes seemed inescapable. Monsieur Pamplemousse's policeman's instincts were roused; the scent of the chase was in his nostrils.

Flinging open the bedroom door, he was about to rush into the corridor when he stopped dead in his tracks.

'*Merde!*'

He felt an enveloping warmth as Elsie cannoned into him from behind. 'What's up?'

'*C'est impossible!*'

Impossible was hardly the word for it. *Merde* upon *merde*! He could scarcely believe his ill fortune. Coming towards him – halfway between his room and the stairs, were two people he recognised. Not only did they come from Paris – that would have been bad enough; but they lived two floors above him in the same apartment block. Recent arrivals, to be sure, but he had met them in the lift on a number of occasions.

'It's them,' hissed Elsie. 'The ones I was telling you about. The ones what was staring at you downstairs.'

Monsieur Pamplemousse signalled for her to go back into the room.

He gave an inward groan. It was too late for him to follow suit. The couple were bearing inexorably down on him, the man already had his hand outstretched in greeting.

'Monsieur Pamplemousse.'

Monsieur Pamplemousse shook his head. Desperate situations demanded desperate measures. On the spur of the moment he decided to brazen it out.

'*Oui.* However, I do not think we have ever met.'

The man looked taken aback. 'You are not Monsieur Aristide Pamplemousse from the *septième étage*?'

'*Non.*'

The couple gazed at him in disbelief. All too well aware of the woman straining to look over his shoulder, Monsieur Pamplemousse glanced round. Elsie was bending over the bed, whiling away the time by smoothing down the cover where he had been sitting. She had her back to them.

Pulling the door shut behind him, he decided that attack was the best form of defence. In any case he had burned his boats. Retreat was now totally out of the question.

'You are from Paris?' he inquired.

'*Oui. Naturellement.* Monsieur Blanche . . . from the ninth floor. My wife . . .'

'Then I fear you must be mistaking me for my twin brother.' Monsieur Pamplemousse cut short the introductions. 'My surname is Pamplemousse, certainly. But my first name is Albert.'

It worked. Disbelief gave way to incredulity, to be followed moments later by a grudging acceptance of the fact that truth was sometimes stranger than fiction.

Though he said it himself, it had to be one of his better essays into the craft of acting. The Director was not the only one capable of thinking on his feet. The only shame was that he couldn't be there to witness it for himself.

Monsieur Blanche raised his hands. '*Mon Dieu!* It is an incredible likeness.'

'In looks only, I fear,' said Monsieur Pamplemousse. 'Deep down we are very different.'

'A thousand pardons, *Monsieur*. I had no idea.'

Monsieur Pamplemousse allowed himself a faint smile of forgiveness. He raised his right hand as though in absolution.

'A not unnatural mistake. It is not the first time. Although I have to admit it is one which hasn't happened for a number of years.

'Aristide and I went our separate ways soon after we left school. He was always the do-gooder, the studious one – his nose for ever buried in a book. Whereas I, I found it impossibly hard to live up to the example he had set. When he was only six he could recite the whole of the Lord's Prayer – backwards.

'Poor Aristide.' Monsieur Pamplemousse found himself warming to his part. 'Is he still doing good works? He should have become a priest, that one. Do you not agree?'

'Not from all I have heard,' said Madame Blanche grimly. Her lips were set in a straight line. They bore an uncanny resemblance to those of Madame Grante in accounts when she was dealing with a particularly problematical P39.

'Oh, really?' Monsieur Pamplemousse stopped in his tracks, curiosity overcoming a desire to make himself scarce as quickly as possible. 'What have you heard?'

'Nothing that bears repeating,' said Madame Blanche firmly. Denied a view of his room, eyeing the torch in his right hand with disfavour, she was doing her best to get a closer look at the polaroid photograph in his other hand. Monsieur Pamplemousse hastily turned it round so that the back was towards her.

'Well, do please remember me to Aristide when you are back in Paris. On second thoughts . . .' Fearing that in his enthusiasm he might have been overdoing things, he had a sudden flash of inspiration. 'Perhaps it is better if you say nothing at all about our meeting, not even to his wife Doucine . . .'

'Doucette,' said Madame Blanche. 'I know her well. We often meet in the launderette.'

'Do you now?' said Monsieur Pamplemousse thoughtfully. He looked Madame Blanche straight in the eye. 'Well, from all I remember of Doucette, she would be most upset. She made Aristide swear never to mention my name again. It will only reopen old wounds.

'And now, *à bientôt.*'

Feeling behind him he made contact with something infinitely softer and more yielding than a doorknob.

'Oooh!' said Elsie. 'You are a one.'

'*Pardon.*' Monsieur Pamplemousse realised all too late that the door to his room had swung open again.

'I was hoping you'd help me with my bra,' said Elsie in her best voice. 'It's been and gone and got itself all twisted. Can't think how it happened.'

Monsieur Pamplemousse found himself hoping the Blanches' command of colloquial English was less than perfect. But at that point fate intervened on his behalf. It manifested itself in the shape of the three Americans he had seen in the restaurant earlier in the evening. They arrived upstairs in a bunch and squeezed their way past without so much as a '*pardon*' or an '*excusez-moi*', leaving in their wake a trail of whiskey fumes and the smell of stale cigars. At close quarters he wouldn't have trusted any one of them more than he could have thrown them – which wouldn't have been very far – and he found himself instinctively checking for his wallet. Doubtless they had fared no better than anyone else in the restaurant, but that didn't excuse bad manners.

He gazed after them as they disappeared round a corner at the far end of the corridor. They were an odd collection. He couldn't help but wonder what strange machinations of fate had brought them to that part of France. They must all have been in their late sixties. Successful in whatever it was they did for a living if the combined weight of gold bracelets and other adornments was anything to go by.

Away from the dining-room they looked even more like fish out of water; they would have been more at home in a night club than in an out of the way sea-side resort: the Negresco in Nice rather than the Hôtel des Dunes in the Landes. Perhaps they had been taken for a ride by their travel agent. If that were the case he wouldn't like to be in the man's shoes when they returned home.

At least the diversion had solved his problem. When he looked round Monsieur and Madame Blanche were heading back along the corridor towards their room. Madame Blanche with scarcely a backward glance, Monsieur Blanche with as many as he could decently get away with.

'What was all that about?' asked Elsie.

'A slight case of mistaken identity, that is all. I thought they would never go.'

'I could tell that,' said Elsie. 'That's why I thought I'd come out and 'elp.'

Monsieur Pamplemousse put the photograph on the table beside his bed for safe keeping, then as soon as the coast was clear he ushered Elsie out of the room and locked the door behind him.

'Quick . . . before they come out again.' The Blanches looked the sort of people who would most likely take a stroll before going to bed. The less he saw of them from now on the better.

He paused on the first landing as a sudden thought struck him.

'Tell me, when did you first notice them?'

Elsie thought for a moment. 'I dunno. They came in half-way through the meal . . . just after Pommes Frites went out.'

'Aah.' Monsieur Pamplemousse breathed a sigh of relief.

He might just get away with pretending to be his own twin brother, but suggesting Pommes Frites was anyone other than Pommes Frites would be pushing things; two pairs of identical twins could be carrying probability to extremes.

It was even more imperative that they find Pommes Frites as soon as possible. If they were seen together his cover would be blown and no two ways about it. From the expression on Madame Blanche's face he might just as well ring Doucette himself and get it over with.

Taking the stairs two at a time, he rushed out into the night leaving Elsie to follow on behind as best she could.

Blissfully unaware of the interest his earlier perambulations had caused, totally uncognisant of the deep waters his master had got himself into, Pommes Frites stirred into action the moment he heard the front door of the hotel open and he recognised the sound of familiar footsteps.

Apart from one brief return trip to the dune, he had been waiting patiently behind a bush for some considerable time, and he was anxious for a spot of action.

For the first half hour or so after leaving the hotel he had been in his element. As far as he was concerned the previous day's outing on the beach at Deauville had been a mere warming-up, a preliminary canter to get the limbs moving. Pleasant enough in its way, and certainly not to be sneezed at, but as nothing compared to the joys of gallivanting about on the Dune du Pilat in the dark.

Finding the '*jambon*' had been an unexpected bonus. Pommes Frites' immediate reaction had been to rush back to his master bearing the evidence of his discovery. Unable to shout 'Eureka! I've found it! as Archimedes had done when he stepped into an overflowing bath and hit on the principle of buoyancy, he had contented himself with a muffled bark or two.

But that had been over half an hour ago. Since then reaction had set in, and during the time at his disposal Pommes Frites had been doing a lot of thinking.

Whilst a long way from being able to claim a laser-sharp mind when it came to working out problems, Pommes Frites was nevertheless blessed with more than his fair share of common sense.

During his time with Monsieur Pamplemousse they had stayed at a great many hotels: some good, some bad. There had been establishments where dogs were treated as welcome guests and others where they were barely tolerated. In most hotels they were able to share a room, but on other occasions such an arrangement had been frowned upon. However, not since the time when they had stayed at an hostelry belonging to an aunt of the Director had the food been quite so abysmally bad. It was not simply abysmally bad; in Pommes Frites' experience it was uniquely abysmally bad.

Since his master was clearly intending to stay for more than one night – Pommes Frites recognised the signs – the unpacking of the bags, the hanging up of clothes – there was only one possible explanation, and Monsieur Pamplemousse's appearing at dinner without a tie confirmed it; they were there for reasons unconnected with work.

Pleased with his deductions, Pommes Frites had rested his brain for a while, at the same time keeping a watchful eye through the window on goings on in the dining-room in case he was missing anything. He saw Monsieur and Madame Blanche arrive. He saw his master and Elsie get up and leave. Soon after that he saw Monsieur and Madame Blanche do likewise.

The rest had done Pommes Frites good. Almost as soon as he returned to his thinking he came up with the answer. If they were not there for reasons connected with work, then they must be there for pleasure. In other words they must be on holiday. Normally if they were on holiday his master would have brought Madame Pamplemousse, but that was a minor point. Pommes Frites decided it was not for him to reason why.

The important fact was that, food apart, they were there to enjoy themselves. It was a time to relax. For the nonce work was a dirty word. Games would be the order of the day, and Pommes Frites decided it should be kept that way.

Pommes Frites knew his master better than most. Give his master a problem and he was liable to retire into himself for days on end with scarcely a word to anyone.

It was his, Pommes Frites' duty, to ensure that didn't happen. Having reached that conclusion he made his second excursion of the evening to the Dune du Pilat.

So it came about that when Monsieur Pamplemousse rushed out of the hotel shouting '*va chercher . . . va chercher . . .* fetch . . . fetch', and then, realising the remaining occupants of the dining-room, having little better to do, were watching his every move with more than a passing interest, did a double take and almost immediately began shouting '*cache-le . . . cache-le . . .* hide . . . hide', Pommes Frites scarcely batted an eyelid.

Clearly it was all part of a new game his master had invented; a variation on hide and seek.

Entering into the spirit of things, Pommes Frites disappeared into the night leaving his master and Elsie to follow on as best they could. Racing up the dune, he steered a course which took him away from the spot where he had first found the *jambon*, whilst at the same time avoiding by a long way the spot where he had reburied it.

Pommes Frites reappeared several times during the following quarter of an hour or so, each time hovering a tantalisingly few metres ahead of his pursuers, before racing on again, leading them higher and higher and further and further away from the hotel.

Monsieur Pamplemousse was the first to crack.

'I think,' he gasped as they paused for breath, 'Pommes Frites is of the opinion that he is, how shall I say? . . . playing a game.'

'I don't know 'ow you say it,' gasped Elsie. 'I think he's being bleeding difficult. If anyone 'ad told me when I left 'ome that I'd find myself chasing a dog up a bloody great 'eap of sand in the dark I'd 'ave told them to get their 'ead seen to. Or, better still, have 'ad mine examined.'

'Life is full of surprises,' said Monsieur Pamplemousse.

'Yeah? Well, I've got one for you,' said Elsie crossly. 'If there's one thing I can't stand about the sea-side it's the bleeding sand. It gets everywhere. It's not my scene. How they stand it in the Foreign Legion I don't know.'

Monsieur Pamplemousse considered the last remark for a moment. The possibility of joining the Foreign Legion to be beside the sea had never occurred to him. He doubted if it had to many of those who had actually taken the plunge and signed along the dotted line.

'I have heard tell that it drives some men mad,' he ventured.

'I'm not surprised,' said Elsie. 'Talk about bleedin' Beau Geste.'

Not for the first time Monsieur Pamplemousse found himself wondering why Elsie had picked on the Hôtel des Dunes for her baptism of fire. A mattress beneath a parasol on the private beach reserved for patrons of the Carlton Hotel in Cannes would have been more up her street. From all the Director had said she could have taken her choice from anywhere in France.

On the other hand he had to agree with her. Running up and down the Dune du Pilat was not his idea of a fun way to spend an evening either. *Montée assez difficile* was how Michelin, with their flair for understatement bordering on pedantry, described it. Monsieur Pamplemousse could have thought up many other alternatives. It would take him a week to get rid of the sand. There was sand in his shoes. There was sand in his hair. There was sand where in the normal scheme of things no sand should ever be allowed to enter.

For a brief moment he would have swapped places with the Director. The Director would have had his portable telephone with him. Assuming the buttons had not been jammed with grit, he would have lost no time in summoning help. Helicopters would have been taking off from Mérignac.

He cast his eyes around. They must be at the highest point of the dune, some hundred metres or so above sea level. The wind had dropped – perhaps because it was now high tide – and the sky was clear. At any other time, and in any other circumstances, it would have merited one of *Le Guide's* Easels – the symbol for an outstanding view. He could see lights twinkling like a giant necklace of pearls strung round the bay as far as Cap Ferret. Behind them lay the Médoc and the vineyards which lined the left bank of the Gironde – the vineyards of St Estephe, Pauillac and St Julien, whose names went around the world.

Between the lighthouse at the end of the peninsula and where they were standing he could dimly make out the darker shape of the Ile aux Oiseaux in the centre of the bay. Fig trees grew there, and tamarisk and sea heliotropes.

He wondered what Brémontier, the architect of the whole scheme, would have thought of it had he still been alive. In carrying out the government's order to stop further erosion from the sea by fixing the soil with low-growing plants, he could hardly have dreamed that in such a short space of time there would be so much change. The Atlantic winds had done more than their share of creating a natural monument to his achievement: two hundred kilometres of fine golden beach now lined the west coast of France.

He caught the sound of a motor boat – probably a local fisherman, and glancing down he thought he saw a glimmer of light from somewhere far below, then it disappeared.

Of Pommes Frites there was neither sight nor sound. He had either given up the game or he was biding his time for a fresh assault.

The dunes rolled away into the distance, unfolding along the seashore as far as the eye could see, and behind them lay the vast forest of the Landes, the largest in Europe, dark and brooding. It was hard to believe that a hundred years ago it hadn't even existed; a wilderness of scrubland and shifting sands and marshes, where the inhabitants walked about on stilts as they tended their flocks of sheep. Now there were over three and half million acres of pine trees. He gave a sigh.

'It is very romantic.'

Elsie took immediate precautions.

'That's as may be,' she said meaningly, 'but I've got a headache.'

Monsieur Pamplemousse was reminded of a remark the Director had made shortly after he'd first introduced Elsie. 'A nice girl, but she suffers a great deal from *mal de tête*.'

At the time he suspected it might have been a case of the Director covering his tracks, but now he wasn't so sure. Elsie was what some of his coarser colleagues would have called a prick-teaser.

'What do you think 'e's done with it?' asked Elsie, breaking into his thoughts.

Monsieur Pamplemousse shrugged. In the excitement he

had almost forgotten the reason for their being there. Perhaps he should have rung the local *Gendarmerie* in the first place. At the time it had seemed sensible to find Pommes Frites first. Now he wasn't so sure.

'Tell you something, if 'e's buried it anywhere round 'ere we'll never find it in a month of Sundays – not unless 'e wants us to.'

Monsieur Pamplemousse had to agree. He knew Pommes Frites of old. Once he had his mind set on something he was not easily diverted.

'What we need,' said Elsie, 'is a late-night butcher's.'

'*Comment?*'

'I've been thinking. If you was to buy a leg of lamb – well, it doesn't 'ave to be lamb, of course – it could be anything. But if you was to do that and give it to 'im it's just possible he might go and bury it in the same place.'

Monsieur Pamplemousse's first inclination was to dismiss the idea as impractical. The possibility of finding anything, let alone a *boucherie* open at that time of night seemed highly unlikely. On the other hand it was better than doing nothing.

Playing for time while he made up his mind he removed a dog whistle from an inside pocket and blew into it.

'Shouldn't think that'll do much good,' said Elsie.

'It is not meant to make a noise,' said Monsieur Pamplemousse. 'It is a silent one.'

'If 'e doesn't come,' said Elsie, 'you'll never know whether it's working or not. You could 'ave got sand in it.'

In the face of feminine logic, Monsieur Pamplemousse gave in. Employing similar thought processes to the ones that Pommes Frites had used earlier, he decided that perhaps Elsie was right. They needed to play him at his own game. They couldn't stay where they were for ever, and Pommes Frites was more than capable of finding his own way back to the hotel.

Given the fact that even as he spoke, Pommes Frites, having also heard the sound of the boat, was making his way slowly and silently down the dune towards the sea, it was a wise decision.

All good things come to an end, and even though it had been one of the best games he had played for ages, a sixth sense told him that it was time to get back to work again. Good resolutions arrived at on his master's behalf disappeared like magic. Nostrils open to catch any scent which might be in the air, his long ears – normally hanging loose in deep folds about his head – alert to every stray sound, slowly and with infinite patience Pommes Frites edged closer and closer to his target.

Patience was a commodity thin on the ground on the other side of the dune. Having not surprisingly drawn a blank in his search for a *boucherie*, or indeed a purveyor of any known form of comestibles, Monsieur Pamplemousse was reading from a menu posted up on the glass door of a small building they had stumbled across.

'*Lundi: laitue, timbale Milanaise, fromage blanc, biscuits.*

'*Mardi: carottes râpées, rôti de boeuf, riz au beurre, glaces.*

'*Jeudi: tomate ou concombre, filets de dinde braisés, petits pois et carottes, Camembert, fruits . . .*'

'Do you 'ave to?' groaned Elsie. 'I'm starving.'

Monsieur Pamplemousse shone his torch through the glass. Picasso-like paintings adorned the walls. A large, brightly coloured wooden railway engine occupied the centre of an uncarpeted room. There was a row of coat hooks fixed to the near side of the engine's boiler. They looked surprisingly close to the ground. He ran his torch along the row and beyond until he reached a row of tiny desks.

'*Alors on a compris*' – the penny had dropped. They were standing outside an infants' school. He looked at the menu again. It was for the week prior to the summer *vacances*.

'I should think they'd bloody need a holiday after all that,' said Elsie, when he told her. 'Poor little buggers. My 'eart bleeds for them, I don't think. It wasn't like it in my day, I can tell you.'

'Nor mine,' agreed Monsieur Pamplemousse. 'And that was much longer ago. Taste classes are now on the National Curriculum.'

When they got back to the hotel he made for his car and felt underneath the driver's seat. Removing a neatly folded sheet of plastic, he attached a small cylinder to a protruding nozzle and pressed a button.

'Blimey!' Elsie watched open-eyed as a kennel began to take shape. 'Whatever will they think of next?'

'It is the only one of its kind,' said Monsieur Pamplemousse proudly. 'I had it specially made.' He took it round to the side of the hotel and found a suitably level piece of ground beneath his room window.

'I think if and when Pommes Frites takes it upon himself to return he should do a bit of guard duty. As for myself . . . I am of the opinion that it is time for bed.'

It also occurred to him that in the circumstances it might be as well to distance himself from Pommes Frites for a while. With luck, Monsieur and Madame Blanche might think he belonged to the hotel.

'Tell you what,' said Elsie. 'How about 'aving a little snack in my room first?'

'You have food?' said Monsieur Pamplemousse. 'In your room?'

'Always look after number one,' said Elsie. 'That's my motto. No one else is going to. It's everyone for theirselves in this world.

'And there's some champagne in the 'fridge. I checked.'

Monsieur Pamplemousse needed no more convincing.

The champagne was a pleasant surprise. It was a half bottle of Billecart-Salmon *rosé*: light, fruity and extremely elegant. After the time spent on the dune it tasted like nectar.

'I daresay we can put it on expenses,' said Elsie.

'Have you met Madame Grante?' asked Monsieur Pamplemousse.

'Who's she when she's at 'ome?' said Elsie.

'The problem is not when she is at home,' said Monsieur Pamplemousse. 'It is when she is in the office. I think perhaps I had better help you with your P39.'

The thought of Elsie doing battle with Madame Grante was an interesting one – he wasn't at all sure who would emerge the victor; the only certainty was that if Madame Grante lost she wouldn't forget. In the end it was he who would be made to suffer.

Elsie opened the fridge door again and removed two packets. The first packet was labelled 'chocolate fingers'. The second, which was covered in translucent plastic material, contained what looked like a selection of small white ceiling tiles edged with brown.

'Good thing I came prepared, innit.' She took a knife and a third packet from the dressing-table drawer.

Monsieur Pamplemousse watched while Elsie spread some butter over one of the tiles.

'What is it?' he asked. 'And where did you find it?'

'It's bread. I brought it with me, dinna I? And am I glad I did!'

Monsieur Pamplemousse wasn't sure whether the last remark was a question or a statement. The English habit of putting an inflection at the end of a sentence, going down in tone rather than up was hard to get used to. Not that Elsie was as big an offender as most. On the whole her voice tended to be on one level. He decided she had made a statement.

'You mean, it is not of today's baking?'

Elsie gave a hollow laugh. 'Today's? Blimey! I doubt if it's last week's. English sliced loaf lasts for ever – just so long as you remember to scrape the green off. That's its strong point.'

'There are others?' inquired Monsieur Pamplemousse. It reminded him of a television documentary he had once seen on the phenomenon of English bread. There had been shots of men squeezing loaves, then standing stop-watch in hand, timing how long it took them to regain their original shape. Taste had not figured largely in the findings.

'It takes all sorts,' said Elsie. 'Just 'cause you don't like sliced loaf don't mean to say it's wrong.

'When I was small,' she continued, 'I used to like granulated sugar on bread and butter. I suppose you get more sophisticated as you grow older.'

Monsieur Pamplemousse couldn't help thinking that despite Elsie's prowess in the kitchen and her undoubted knowledge of certain areas relating to matters of food, she was not Inspector material. No one could possibly like sliced bread coated with *sucre*. He watched while she took one of the chocolate fingers from the packet, laid it on a slice of buttered bread, then rolled it up to form a baton. It was hard to imagine what kind of symbol they might use in *Le Guide* to denote a restaurant specialising in such things. If it looked at all like the one Elsie was holding, the chances were it might give potential customers the wrong idea.

'Does it have a name?' he asked politely.

'It's a chocolate-finger sandwich, innit,' said Elsie. 'I mean, what else would you call it?'

'It looks very sustaining,' said Monsieur Pamplemousse. He took a tentative bite. Although he was loth to admit the fact, it tasted much nicer than he had expected. The second bite was even nicer.

'When I was small I used to enjoy eating raw *croissant* mixture dipped in *confiture*.'

'There you are,' said Elsie. She handed him a third baton.

'I think perhaps I will take it back to my room for later,' said Monsieur Pamplemousse.

'You're a poppet,' said Elsie unexpectedly. As he stood up to leave she planted a large, wet kiss on his forehead. 'Nightie, night, sweet repose. All the pillow, all the clothes. See you in the morning.'

Outside in the corridor, clasping the chocolate-finger roll like a weapon in his hand, the inevitable happened. He heard voices in the hall. His timing couldn't have been worse if he'd tried. A moment later Monsieur and Madame Blanche came into view, returning from their walk. Monsieur Pamplemousse gave them a good-night wave with his free hand as they followed him up the stairs.

It occurred to him that he had ways of making Madame Blanche sniff.

Back in his room he gazed at his reflection in the mirror. He had chocolate round his mouth and lipstick on his forehead.

Hearing more voices outside and the sound of a door slamming he crossed to the window and looked out. He was just in time to see what must be old Pierre – the newly incumbent chef – leaving the hotel. His back was bent and he was walking slowly, lurching slightly from side to side as though in a dream. As he mounted his bicycle and wobbled off into the night he looked a broken man.

Monsieur Pamplemousse closed the shutters. Worn out by the combined effect of the long drive from Paris and by the

73

evening's exertions, he decided to leave telephoning the police until the morning. He wasn't sure what he was going to tell them anyway and he simply couldn't face the thought of long explanations.

But despite feeling tired, sleep eluded him – he had far too many things on his mind; Elsie . . . Pommes Frites' strange behaviour . . . the Director's warning, cut off in mid-sentence . . . his own new identity . . .

He wondered how he and Elsie would spend the rest of the week . . . tomorrow they could drive into Arcachon . . . he would have to go there anyway to report Pommes Frites' find . . .

Once, when he had almost dozed off, he was nudged awake again by the sound of a car back-firing in the distance – a sudden sharp crack like a gun going off.

It took him a while to settle down again. He wondered if Madame Blanche would say anything to Doucette. If she had half a chance she would. He would meet that problem when it happened. In the meantime he had to admit there was a certain attraction about his new role.

It was perhaps half an hour or so later that he heard a car arrive at the hotel. He groped for the torch and checked the time on his watch. It was a little after one o'clock. Doors slammed, followed shortly afterwards by footsteps on the stairs. He guessed it must be the Americans returning from a night out.

They paused outside his door and he heard whispering. He was beginning to wish he'd let Elsie have his room after all. For some reason the top floor of the hotel far outweighed the first in the popularity stakes. Perhaps everyone was hoping for a view of the sea.

Monsieur Pamplemousse couldn't have put a time to when he finally fell asleep, but it seemed only a matter of moments before he was woken yet again, this time with a vague feeling of unease. It took him a moment or two to force himself properly awake. He switched on the light. A quick glance at his watch showed him it was now two-twenty. He was about to sink back on to his pillow when he heard a whining noise from somewhere outside his window.

Jumping out of bed, he flung open the shutters intending to remonstrate in no uncertain terms about dogs who stayed out late without their master's permission, when he paused. The moon was hidden behind some trees, but even in the shadow there was something familiar about the way Pommes Frites was standing.

Returning a moment later with his torch, Monsieur Pamplemousse trained it on the area below his window and pressed the switch. As he did so he caught his breath.

It was, in many respects, a duplicate of the scene Elsie had captured earlier in the evening; a scene which he had already irreverently labelled in his mind as 'Pommes Frites with *jambon*'.

Bidding Pommes Frites to remain exactly where he was, Monsieur Pamplemousse disappeared from the window. He returned a moment later with Elsie's photograph. It needed only a simple comparison between Pommes Frites' latest find and that shown in the picture to confirm his worst suspicions.

In all but one respect the salient features of the *jambon* were remarkably similar; in size, shape, and by virtue of being encased in a white, cotton material. However, unless Monsieur Bouet had been a singularly careless dresser, or had by some unfortunate quirk of nature been endowed with two right feet, then the inescapable conclusion was that Pommes Frites had discovered yet another *jambon*, for the end of his latest find was encased not in a wooden sabot, but in a rope-soled canvas pump.

5
THE SEVENTH DWARF

'Cheer up,' said Elsie. 'It may never happen.'

Monsieur Pamplemousse broke off a morsel of bread from a slice of *baguette* and eyed it through eyes weary from lack of sleep. There was a certain lack of crispness in the crust which summed up his own state of mind.

'I'm afraid it already has. You can hardly call finding two dead bodies in one night a non-event.'

'They weren't your actual bodies,' said Elsie. She leaned across the table and patted him consolingly. 'Only bits and pieces like, and you haven't even got those any more. Well, not until Pommes Frites finds them again. *If* he ever does. No wonder he looks gloomy. He's worse than you are.'

'Pommes Frites often looks gloomy,' said Monsieur Pamplemousse defensively, 'but that doesn't mean to say he is unhappy. Although he may well be so at the moment. I think he is suffering from a sense of failure.'

'I'm not surprised,' said Elsie. 'Fancy not being able to find his *jambons*. Fine bloodhound 'e is.'

'It is hardly his fault that a wind sprang up during the night,' said Monsieur Pamplemousse. 'Any trails there might have been disappeared in the sand. I defy anyone to find them. Also, he is probably unhappy because he thinks I have been avoiding him and he is at a loss to understand why.'

'And have you?'

'In a way, yes. But only because I think the less we are seen together the better. I doubt if Madame Blanche would accept that my twin brother also owns an identical blood-hound. Several times I have had to send Pommes Frites on his way in case I got caught with him. This morning, when I heard the Blanches approaching, I had to push him out of the window before he had finished his *croissant*. He was most upset. I should have taken *petit déjeuner* in my room.'

'I'm glad I'm not married if that's the way you 'ave to carry on,' said Elsie. 'It sounds to me as though you're up the creek without a paddle.'

'That is one way of putting it,' said Monsieur Pamplemousse. 'In France we say "*être dans le pétrin*".'

It had not been the happiest of nights. No sooner had he got back to bed than he'd heard a scream coming from Elsie's room. Others had heard it too, but he had reached her first – rather to his regret. Clearly the worst of interpretations had been placed, not only on his presence, but on what he appeared to be doing. Disentangling high-heeled shoes which had become deeply enmeshed in the seat of a wicker-work chair was no easy task – particularly at three o'clock in the morning. It was a wonder Elsie hadn't gone straight through and done herself permanent damage.

He glanced across at her. She must have a thing about standing on chairs. It was curious how someone who was able to take the earlier events in her stride should go into a state of collapse at the sight of a spider. That was her story anyway.

In the end he had done the decent thing and let her have his room for the remainder of the night.

It had not been the happiest of days either. The Police had been less than grateful when he bid them *adieu* that afternoon. A day spent tramping up and down the dunes had left no one in the best of tempers, least of all the contingent of 'volunteers' from the local *gendarmerie*. Their hearts had never been in it, and viewing the Dune du Pilat by daylight and at close quarters it was easy to see why. Pommes Frites had not been high in their popularity stakes. The fact that other dogs brought in from Bordeaux had fared no better counted for nothing. Scepticism had been rife among the rank and file; their plastic bags had gone back to Headquarters unopened. Only Elsie's polaroid picture saved them from total ignominy, providing as it did the one shred of evidence that the whole thing had not been part of a bad dream on Monsieur Pamplemousse's part.

The fact that it also provided the Police with the first positive clue as to the fate of what must by now be regarded as the late Monsieur Bouet, counted for nothing. That it had been a genuine part of him was confirmed in no uncertain manner by Madame Bouet, whose decline when she saw the photograph and identified the sabot reached a new low and was audible far beyond the confines of her apartment adjoining the Hôtel des Dunes.

Circumstantial evidence provided by Monsieur Pamplemousse himself pointed to Pommes Frites' second find as being an equally essential part of Monsieur Bouet's underling, Pierre. Really, the Police had no cause to grumble at receiving such an unexpected bonus, but that hadn't stopped them. Congratulations on a job well done were not forthcoming. Murmurs of appreciation for Monsieur Pamplemousse's public spiritedness in volunteering the information were muted to the point of inaudibility.

He was also having doubts about the wisdom of not

revealing his true identity. On the spur of the moment, seeing
a glint of recognition in the eyes of the *officier* in charge of
the investigation at the name Pamplemousse, it had seemed a
good idea to take advantage of his newly acquired identity.
Warming to the idea, he'd tended to over-embroider the part
of a twin brother rather than play it down. Signing the statement had set the seal on his folly. There was no going back.
In the old days, if their positions been reversed and the truth
had come to light, he would have thrown the book at the other
party.

'You could take him to a dog parlour and 'ave him dyed
black,' said Elsie, breaking into his thoughts. 'That'd kill
two birds with one stone. The Blanches wouldn't recognise
'im and he'd really 'ave something to look gloomy about
then.'

'Bloodhounds always look morose,' said Monsieur Pamplemousse. 'In repose it is their natural expression. It simply
happens to be worse than usual at the moment.'

As if to reinforce his statement, a deep sigh issued from
beneath the table. It was Pommes Frites' way of pointing out
that a), in an ideal world conversation ought to take place
after a meal rather than before it, and b), in his humble opinion too much emphasis was being placed on eating in restaurants where fish predominated.

'Gives me the creeps,' said Elsie. 'I wouldn't like to be
shipwrecked on a desert island with 'im, I must say. 'E'd be a
right bundle of laughs, I don't think.'

They ate in silence for a while. Elsie's mind was clearly
elsewhere. He fell to wondering about her and what sort
of life she led back in England. It was hard to envisage.
Outwardly she was confident and well organised, frighten-
ingly so at times. It was hard to picture her at home doing
the dusting. On the other hand, the snack in her room the pre-

vious evening had revealed a totally different side to her character. It had made him warm towards her, as though he had been let in on a guilty secret, which in a way he supposed he had.

Elsie was dressed rather more discreetly than had been the case the previous evening. The off-the-shoulder number must have suffered on the dunes. By comparison, her latest outfit, in plain, unadorned black wool, wouldn't have looked out of place on a nun about to take her final exams. Even so, her habit of leaning across the table whenever she had something important to say would have brought a worried frown to even the most broad-minded of Mother Superiors overseeing her practicals, as would the accompanying waft of quietly expensive perfume. Someone, somewhere, must be keeping Elsie in the style to which she had clearly become accustomed.

Her presence certainly didn't go unnoticed by the other occupants of the restaurant where they were dining. At the Paris Lido it would have been eye-catching; in Arcachon it was little short of sensational.

Monsieur Pamplemousse wasn't at all sorry the owners, in ploughing much of their profit back into the business in the form of designer vegetation, had also been fortunate enough to engage the services of someone with green fingers. Ivy formed a screen around their table; passion flowers grew rampant; tradescantia trailed where others failed to grow. From time to time he was aware of eyes peering through gaps in the foliage. It was worse than dining in some South American jungle surrounded by hostile natives who had never seen a white woman before. He regretted not bringing a can of fly spray. Had he done so, he would have been sorely tempted to use it.

The Restaurant Joséphine was as unlike the Hôtel des Dunes

as it was possible to be. In fairness, they had a head start; at the current rate of scoring, two heads. The *patron* was hard at work in the kitchen – every so often he caught sight of a man in a white hat peering round a corner to see how things were going out front. Madame Joséphine, despite Elsie's disparaging 'mutton dressed as lamb', was ever-present and solicitous.

They ordered *pâté de foie gras*. It came with a glass of chilled *demi-sec* Vouvray – a perfect accompaniment. To follow, they chose grilled sea bass. It was presented on a bed of dried fennel. A waiter arrived clasping an amber bottle. Flamed in Cognac, the stalks of the fennel imparted a scent which flavoured the whole dish. Inspired by the first course, Monsieur Pamplemousse consulted the *carte des vins* again and changed his order from a Muscadet to an older Vouvray. There was only a token mention of Burgundy.

The dessert was a toss-up between *Iles flotantes, Crème brûlée, Tarte maison* and *Mousse au chocolat à l'orange*. They both chose the mousse. It came with a separate bowl of cream which was left on the table. The chocolate was satisfactorily dark and bitter, and the faint taste of orange gave it a certain distinction, lifting it above the norm.

'How would you rate the meal?' asked Monsieur Pamplemousse as Elsie licked her spoon clean.

'The *pâté* was all right,' said Elsie. 'But it was round. I reckon it came from a tin. The sea bass was great, but then, there's no reason why it shouldn't have been. The olive oil on the salad was too cold – probably straight out of the fridge. If it had been warmer it would have brought out the flavour more. I reckon a Wrought-Iron Table and Chair – plus.'

Monsieur Pamplemousse nodded his approval. It tallied with the current entry in *Le Guide*. It was a cut above a Bar

Stool – the symbol for a good place to stop *en route*. He wondered if Elsie had checked it herself before they came out. Then he dismissed the idea. She had left the booking to him.

'Some of my favourite restaurants are in that category. They are the backbone of French cuisine.

'I have never eaten here before, but the owner is in his late fifties – a few years older than *Madame*. I would guess they have been here most of their lives. The menu has probably hardly changed since they began. They get their fish practically straight out of the ocean. You are right . . . the *patron* has probably cooked sea bass so many times he could do it with his eyes shut.'

'No Stock Pot?'

'*Non*.' Monsieur Pamplemousse shook his head. 'The menu is too limited for that. Besides, to award a Stock Pot to a restaurant such as this would do the patron a grave disservice. Here he is, happy in what he does, wanting no more than to earn an honest living. He has his faithful band of regulars. They come here because they know what to expect and would doubtless go elsewhere if they didn't get their *soupe de poisson* on Thursdays or their lobster *cassoulet* on Saturday evening. If he had a Stock Pot his costs would treble or even quadruple overnight. He would have to take on more staff, particularly in the kitchen. People from outside the town, from Paris, from other parts of the world, would seek him out. He would need to appoint at least one assistant chef and train him in his ways, otherwise he could never afford to be ill or take a day off. He would have to find accommodation for them. Then he would need to invest heavily in wine. The present list is much too short and parochial. Life would never be the same. And once having been awarded a Stock Pot, he would live in fear of losing it.

'In the case of a three-Stock-Pot restaurant the problem is much worse. It is one of the reasons why so many chefs branch out into other areas - to make the whole thing pay. I know chefs who would sooner not have the award. Success in life is a mixed blessing. Often you find you have mounted a treadmill from which there is no escape.'

Elsie looked at him curiously. 'What made you become an Inspector?'

Monsieur Pamplemousse shrugged. 'Fate. I resigned from my previous post and quite by chance, on the very day that I left, with no idea of what I was going to do – or even *could* do, I happened to bump into the Director.'

'Funny thing, fate,' said Elsie. 'I mean – like us being here this evening. In fact, everyone being here come to that.'

'It is the same with the hotel,' said Monsieur Pamplemousse. 'I often wonder what brings people to a certain spot at one particular moment in time.'

'Yeah. Well . . . like I said, it's fate. I suppose . . .' Elsie looked for a moment as though she was about to develop her thesis, but then Madame Joséphine arrived with the coffee and a plate of *tuiles dentelles*.

Monsieur Pamplemousse waited until she had departed before continuing the conversation.

'What do you think of it? The hotel, I mean. You will need to make out a report. It will be difficult in the circumstances, but it will be a good exercise. I will go through the form with you tomorrow. There are categories for everything, from the car-parking facilities to the quality of the bed linen, from ease of access for those who are incapacitated to the view from the room. It is several hours' work.'

'I know one thing,' said Elsie. 'The Hotel's not like what it said in the brochure.'

'They often aren't,' said Monsieur Pamplemousse drily. 'A

84

wide-angle lens and a good imagination can work wonders.'

''Alf a kilometre to the sea,' said Elsie bitterly. 'They didn't say nuffin' about there being a bleedin' great pile of sand in the way. You can't see it even if you stand on a chair.'

'An unfortunate oversight,' said Monsieur Pamplemousse. 'Why did you choose this hotel? I'm surprised they even have a brochure.'

'It was Reginald's idea,' said Elsie.

'Reginald?'

'My boy friend. He'd heard it was interesting down 'ere. Only he couldn't come 'isself.'

'He is a food Inspector?'

'Reginald?' Elsie gave a hollow laugh. 'He wouldn't know one end of a sausage from the other.'

She looked around the restaurant as though anxious to change the subject. 'I wouldn't mind being in this business.'

Memories of the one meal Elsie had cooked the night he and Doucette had dined with the Director came flooding back. It had definitely been Stock Pot material.

'I am sure you would be very good at it.' Monsieur Pamplemousse helped himself to a *tuile*. 'I'm sure you'd do better than these. They are much too soft to the touch. Another reason for not recommending a Stock Pot.'

'They were probably made this morning,' said Elsie. 'Can't say as I blame him. You can't do everything at once. That's the trouble. If Reginald and me opened a restaurant I'd be stuck in the kitchen all day long, slaving over a hot stove while 'e did the chatting up. I can picture it all.'

'Does he have any particular interests?'

'Interests? Reginald's interested in anything that makes money. Buying and selling mostly. Import and export. This, that and the other.'

'What sort of things?' Monsieur Pamplemousse found

himself growing more and more intrigued. It was like playing some kind of guessing game.

'Well . . . let's say he's got 'is finger on what people want and he knows where to get it. But not in the kind of way your Paris friend would be interested in.'

'My Paris friend?'

'You know. That art dealer you was spinning a yarn to yesterday evening.'

'Monsieur Blanche? How do you know he is an art dealer?'

'Well – whatever. He was standing in front of that painting on the landing this morning making notes. And he 'ad his camera and a magnifying glass with him. I reckon he's got 'is eye on it.'

'Do you now?'

''Course, it's not like dealing in jewels. Reginald always says that jewels combine the maximum wealth in the smallest possible space.'

'Madame Chanel said much the same thing,' said Monsieur Pamplemousse drily.

'Well, she would, wouldn't she? It's all right for some. She probably didn't 'ave much trouble going through customs.

'That's where jewels have the advantage. There's all sorts of places you can stick them so as other people won't see - not unless they're poking their nose into places where they shouldn't be, if you know what I mean. Not like a painting, unless it's a miniature of course.'

Monsieur Pamplemousse was beginning to feel a little out of his depth. A sudden thought struck him.

'Monsieur Blanche is not the only one to have taken a photograph of the picture.'

The blue in Elsie's eyes took on a metallic tint; momentarily more cobalt than azure. 'Well, it's nice innit.' Helping herself to another *tuile*, she bent it almost double between her fingers and thumb. 'I see what you mean. Still, the coffee's all right. I always think there's nothing worse than a bad cup of coffee at the end of a meal. Spoils the whole evening.'

Taking the hint, Monsieur Pamplemousse withdrew his note-pad and took the opportunity to jot down a few notes.

'So where did you get your know-how from?' asked Elsie.

'I have always been interested in food. I was lucky enough to have a mother who was a born cook. Then I spent some time attached to the Paris food fraud squad while I was with the Sûreté. It gave me an insight into what can be done if you are that way inclined. Putting margarine into *croissants au beurre*; using walnut juice to dye Moroccan white sand truffles black and then passing them off as the real thing; butchers fiddling their scales and selling short weight . . .'

Monsieur Pamplemousse broke off and looked across the table with some concern as Elsie started to choke. 'Let me get you some water.'

'While you were doing *what*?' gasped Elsie.

'Did *Monsieur le Directeur* not tell you? I was with the Paris Sûreté for many years. I joined them soon after I left school.'

'You're not still with them, are you?' demanded Elsie. 'I mean . . . like . . . attached as it were.'

Monsieur Pamplemousse shook his head. 'After I resigned I severed all my connections.' It was the short answer and the simplest.

Elsie looked relieved.

'What made you do it? Resign, I mean.'

'I had a little trouble with some girls at the Folies . . .'

'You mean there was more than one?'

'Fifteen,' said Monsieur Pamplemousse.

'Blimey!' Elsie looked at him with renewed interest and something akin to respect. 'I can't wait to 'ear more.'

'There is nothing much to hear,' said Monsieur Pamplemousse. 'It was literally a case of my being caught with my trousers down. Someone gave me a knock-out drop and left me locked in a cupboard above the chorus girls' dressing room. When I came round my clothes had been stolen and there was a cine camera . . . with some exposed film . . . someone had bored a hole through the ceiling. It was what is known as a "put-up job".'

'Of course,' said Elsie.

'You do not have to believe me,' said Monsieur Pamplemousse stiffly.

'I believe you,' said Elsie simply.

'*Merci*. No one else did at the time, and I had little recourse but to resign. That is how Pommes Frites and I met - he had just been made redundant following a cut-back and they gave him to me as a farewell present.'

For years the ignominy had followed him around. 'Doing a Pamplemousse' had become a synonym in the force for scandalous behaviour. For a time he had even thought of changing his name. It was one of the reasons for his prevarication at the *gendarmerie* that morning; the certain knowledge that revealing his true identity would have given rise to nudges and winks and barely suppressed guffaws.

'I thought you French were supposed to be broad-minded.'

'It is true that we are perhaps less hypocritical about these things than some.' Monsieur Pamplemousse avoided the phrase 'two-faced'. 'But there was another factor. One of the girls had been got at and was prepared, if necessary, to swear that certain acts of a bizarre nature had taken place. I wished to spare my wife that.'

'Dear, oh dear,' said Elsie. 'Well, I never. I don't know what Reginald will say when I tell him. It's a bit "them and us" as far as 'e's concerned.'

'Is it necessary that he should know?' asked Monsieur Pamplemousse.

'I suppose not,' said Elsie dubiously. 'It's just that Reginald's a dab hand at getting things out of me and he gets upset if I don't tell 'im everything.'

'And he would consider me one of "them"?'

'Once a copper – always a copper – that's what Reginald says.'

Monsieur Pamplemousse refrained from replying that in his opinion the reverse was also true. Instead he called for the bill.

All the same, he had to admit there was a certain amount of truth in the saying. As they left the restaurant and began walking down the street towards the boulevard de la Plage where he had left his car, he found himself automatically looking around with a policeman's eye, making a mental note of shop windows, the way people walked and dressed, vehicle registrations.

The white exterior of the Casino de la Plage came into view and he pointed to a car parked just inside the gates. It had a Hertz sign stuck to the windscreen.

'We are not the only ones in Arcachon from the hotel. The Americans are also here.'

'Ooh, can we go in too?' Elsie slipped her arm into his and gave it a squeeze. 'Please. I don't know when I last 'ad a flutter.'

Monsieur Pamplemousse hesitated. *Chiens* would not be admitted. There was no doubt in his mind that he would incur further opprobrium from Pommes Frites if he consigned him to the car for the rest of the evening. His emergency biscuits were back at the hotel, and leaving the radio on would be no compensation. On the other hand . . . He wondered if Elsie had the ability to change the colour of her eyes at will. They were now the lightest of blue: as light as the touch of her thigh against his.

Avoiding Pommes Frites' gaze, Monsieur Pamplemousse opened the car door and ushered him into the back seat.

The interior of the Casino was a duplicate of all casinos everywhere. He could have described it without going inside. The marble staircase, the thick carpet, the chandeliers, the staff who looked as though they spent their entire lives in evening dress.

Having registered, he waited while Elsie went through the formality of producing her passport. As soon as she had received an entrance card she disappeared into the *toilette* to put on her 'war paint'. When she came out he noticed she was wearing a thin gold chain round her neck with a single diamond set in a horseshoe-shaped mounting. She also had on a pair of matching earrings.

Entering the gaming room was like taking a step back into the thirties. Dark corners were non-existent. Doubtless there were hidden television cameras monitoring their every movement – the 'eye-in-the-sky'. Video recorders would be in operation. He caught the familiar sound of the ivory ball against the spinning roulette wheel, punctuated every so often by the sharp riffling of cards. In the restaurant he'd been the only one with a tie and he'd felt out of place, now he was glad he had worn one. Less chic than Deauville – where the Director was probably ensconced at that very moment and where jackets and ties would be *de rigueur* – it was still a place where people dressed as for an occasion.

As he escorted Elsie towards the bar Monsieur Pamplemousse glanced around the room. Most of the tables were already crowded. There were several small groups of Japanese men present, their faces as expressionless as those belonging to the card dealers themselves. He wondered where they went to in the day-time – he couldn't remember seeing any parties of Japanese when he and Elsie had driven through Arcachon the day before.

He pulled up two stools. 'What will you have?'

'Adam's Ale,' said Elsie.

'*Qu'est-ce que c'est?*'

'Aqua pura. Water. I want to keep a straight 'ead. Back in a minute.'

Reflecting that Elsie was full of surprises, Monsieur Pamplemousse ordered a Badoit. It cost more than his *vin rouge*. Come to think of it, she hadn't drunk much at dinner either.

Wondering if she had planned to visit the casino all along, he watched as she strolled over to one of the *vingt-et-un* tables where the Americans were playing. They were concentrating on the game. Although it was too early for any really high play, it looked serious. They had obviously come prepared, for they were all in evening dress. Short, thick-set, hair close-cropped, they could have been taken for extras in a pre-war gangster movie.

After a while Elsie left the table and went across to a *caisse* at the far end of the room. She returned clutching a handful of plastic chips. From where he was sitting Monsieur Pamplemousse couldn't see their value.

The Americans parted to let her in as she rejoined their table and for a while she was lost from view. For someone who hadn't visited a casino in a long time she seemed very much at home.

Monsieur Pamplemousse sipped his drink and turned his attention to the rest of the room.

There was a certain fascination in watching the speed at which the croupiers worked, just as there was in watching anyone who was highly skilled and professional. Their rakes

91

moved faster than a serpent's tongue as they cleared the tables after each turn of the wheel, tossing counters back into the appropriate squares with uncanny accuracy.

Once a copper – always a copper. It was a fact that trouble seemed to follow him around, but it was equally true to say that over the years he had developed a nose for it. Perhaps the reverse applied; it was he who attracted the trouble.

Sitting at the end of each roulette table were two men – the *Chef de partie* and his assistant. Dark-suited, anonymous, unsmiling and completely interchangeable, watching every movement of the play: those of the croupiers as well as the punters. It would be hard to get away with anything. One whiff of suspicion and next time you would be politely but firmly refused admission. The odds were always on the house.

It was also a fact that when he first joined the force he had found himself isolated from many of his old friends. True, he had made new ones, but he had realised very quickly that it would always be a case of 'us' and 'them' – of his being on the other side of the fence in many people's eyes.

Draining his glass as Elsie rejoined him, he pointed to hers. 'You won't change your mind?'

'No, thanks, ta ever so.' Elsie took a swig of her Badoit and then felt in her handbag. 'Take this. It'll pay for the meal.'

Monsieur Pamplemousse looked at the pile of notes on the bar counter and shook his head. '*Le Guide* will be paying. Provided we make out a report I will claim it on expenses. That is why we are here.'

'Go on,' said Elsie. 'There'll be plenty more where that came from before the night's out. I'm on to a winning streak.'

'You are staying? Wouldn't it be better to leave while you are ahead? Winning streaks don't last for ever. It is a battle

between you and the casino and they always win in the end.'
He tried not to make it sound too holier-than-thou.

'Reginald wouldn't agree. He says gambling is a battle
between you and yourself.'

Monsieur Pamplemousse sighed. He was beginning to feel
that if anyone ever published a book of the sayings of Reginald, he ought to be in line for an autographed copy.

'Why don't you go on back?' said Elsie. 'I'll be all right. I
can get a taxi.' She snapped her handbag shut and held up the
back of her right hand to be kissed. 'Be good. And if you
can't be good – be careful.'

'I was about to give you the same advice,' said Monsieur
Pamplemousse. 'If you need any help, you know where I am.'

'*A bientôt,* as they say.' Elsie fluttered her eyelashes and
kissed him lightly in return.

Not unaware that he probably had lipstick on his brow, but
hesitant about removing it with his handkerchief in case he
forgot about it later, Monsieur Pamplemousse made his way
out of the casino and back to the car. He felt curiously de-
flated. There was no reason why Elsie should wish to spend
the evening with him, and yet he couldn't rid himself of the
feeling that in some way he had been used.

Apart from a few pockets of light from out-of-town restaurants, he drove through darkness most of the way back to the
Hôtel des Dunes. Arcachon went to bed early.

His mood was not improved by Pommes Frites, who showed
his disapproval of the whole evening by pointedly shifting his
weight around whenever they turned a corner, going with the
tilt of the car rather than against it, so that on several occasions they nearly turned over.

The hotel car park looked deserted. The English family had
left early that morning. The Blanches' Renault was there and
so was the Mercedes belonging to the German couple.

The lights were on in the foyer, but there was no other sign of life. Maurice, the general dogsbody, was conspicuous by his absence. Having been up since before dawn attending to the *petit déjeuner* he'd probably gone to bed early. At least he hadn't locked up.

Monsieur Pamplemousse went behind the desk and removed his key from a row of hooks on the wall behind it. In a cubby-hole beneath it there was a slip of paper with a message to telephone the Director as soon as possible.

On the way up the stairs he paused halfway and took a long look at the painting. He was no expert, but it did have a certain 'something'. It could be a copy of an early Impressionist – a Sisley perhaps. It really needed to be seen in daylight and from a distance to get the full effect. He wished now he'd brought a flash attachment for his camera.

Back in his room he closed the shutters, picked up the telephone and dialled the Director's number. It was answered on the first ring.

'Pamplemousse! Where have you been? I have been trying to reach you all the evening.' Once again the Director's voice had a muffled sound.

'I have been out for a meal, *Monsieur*. Then Elsie expressed a desire to visit the casino.'

'She is with you now, I trust?'

'*Monsieur*, I am in my room. What are you suggesting?'

'No, no, Pamplemousse. You misunderstand me. I am merely asking you if she is at the hotel.'

'I left her at the casino, *Monsieur*.'

There was a sharp intake of breath from the other end.

'Alone? That is not good news.'

'But, *Monsieur*, I am hardly her keeper . . .'

'Aristide . . . yesterday I received a telephone call from *Angleterre*. I was trying to tell you about it last night when we were interrupted. Whoever it was refused to give a name, but there were strange noises going on in the background – shouts, and what sounded like someone drawing a stick across some bars. All the voice said was "Look after Else . . . or else". It was most confusing. When I asked which Else he meant, the caller hung up. Frankly, I am worried. What do you think it can mean?'

'I have no idea, *Monsieur*.' The thought of there being two Elsies was not one he wished to entertain for the moment.

'I charge you with her safety, Aristide.'

'But, *Monsieur*, she is a big girl . . . well able to look after herself . . .' The *débâcle* with the card trick came back to him.

'I know she is a big girl, Pamplemousse . . .' The Director paused for a moment, clearly drawing on his store of memories. 'I am also well aware that in the normal course of events she is more than able to look after herself. All I am saying . . .' There was a click followed by the dialling tone.

Monsieur Pamplemousse gazed at the receiver in his hand for a moment or two before replacing it in its cradle.

Pommes Frites looked at him inquiringly. Ever sensitive to the moods of others, he could tell that something was exercising his master's mind. Not one to harbour rancour for any length of time, particularly with those he loved, he stood up and wagged his tail sympathetically.

Monsieur Pamplemousse took the hint. Pommes Frites was right. It was time for a walk. In times of stress there was nothing like a good walk to clear the mind.

The wind which had got up during the previous night had dropped again and the air on top of the dunes was as clear as it was possible to be. The tide was neither in nor out. From where he stood he could see the waves shimmering in the moonlight as they broke gently along the line of the beach, but they were too far away for the sound to reach him.

He sat down on the sand for a while, going over in his mind the conversation he'd had with the Director. Despite Elsie's grumbles, he couldn't help liking her. No one could possibly accuse her of being negative or standoffish. He had to admit he missed her company. Mentally tossing a coin, he wondered if he ought to go back into Arcachon and make sure she was all right. It came down tails. She would hardly thank him if he did turn up at the casino. Clearly she had wanted to be left to her own devices, and she might well suspect the worst if he reappeared.

Suddenly aware that Pommes Frites was pricking up his ears, Monsieur Pamplemousse concentrated his attention closer to home. At first he could detect nothing, then gradually he heard the soft crunching sound of footsteps in the sand. It was accompanied by heavy breathing. Every few moments it stopped altogether as whoever was responsible paused for a rest. He caught the glimmer of a flashlight.

Signalling Pommes Frites to lie low, Monsieur Pamplemousse flattened himself against the sand. It felt surprisingly warm. He was none too soon. A moment later the bent figure of a man came into view, making heavy weather of the last few metres of the climb before he reached the summit. Head down, he passed by them some ten metres or so away, then rapidly gathered speed, slithering from side to side as he headed back down the way they had just come.

Watching the gnome-like figure as it disappeared in the direction of the hotel, Monsieur Pamplemousse was irresistibly reminded of a scene from *Snow White and the Seven Dwarfs*. The only difference being the figure wasn't wearing a miner's lamp, and the occasional gleam came not from the head of a pick, but from moonlight striking the handle of a metal detector he was carrying over his shoulder. Neither Dopey nor Sneezy, not Bashful or Doc, and certainly not Happy;

Monsieur Blanche looked extremely grumpy and ready for sleep.

6
THE CAST ASSEMBLES

Monsieur Pamplemousse came out of the *gendarmerie* in Arcachon and joined Pommes Frites who had been waiting patiently on the steps. He paused to breathe in the fresh air, then glanced at his watch. It said 10.34. The sun was already above the top of the buildings on the other side of the street. The best of a glorious July morning had been wasted in the tedium of getting things down on paper. A course in speed-writing wouldn't have come amiss. If he'd had anything to do with the matter he would have had a go at the man taking notes in an attempt to wean him off pencil-licking. He suspected the *officier* in charge of the case was being deliberately slow. Several times he'd looked as though he had been on the point of saying something revealing, and each time it boiled down to going over the same old ground once again.

What was he doing in Arcachon? When had he arrived? Had he driven straight down from Paris? What was his occupation? If he lived in the Auvergne what had he been doing in Paris?

Questions, questions, questions.

The more the *officier* persisted, the more stubborn Monsieur Pamplemousse became, safe in the knowledge that they could hardly accuse him of any crime. Once again, he had conveniently forgotten his *carte d'identité*, making a great show of searching through his pockets, grimacing and 'poofing' as he went. He wouldn't get away with it a third time. The twenty-four hours' grace he had been given in which to produce it would go all too quickly, and then what? He would meet that problem when it happened.

All in all, Monsieur Pamplemousse felt the outrage of a man caught out concocting a story which he had told so well he'd come to believe in it himself. His twin brother had become so real in his mind, it seemed positively insulting to query his existence.

Ever sensitive to his master's vicissitudes, and anxious to register support and sympathy, Pommes Frites left his mark on the wheel of a police car parked outside the entrance. As he followed Monsieur along rue Georges Hameau and across rue Général Leclerc towards the railway station where the car had been left he recognised the signs of a pensive mind at work: the wandering gait, the hands in the pockets, the absentminded air of a man lost in thought.

There were two games of *boules* in progress on the sandy area between the road and the *gare*. They were probably a permanent fixture. The first was made up of a group of old hands – retired fishermen to a man if their wind-dried faces were anything to go by – and the second a bevy of younger players, among them two women. A sign of the times if ever there was one. Where would it all end? His old father would have died of shock; his mother would have said they were no better than they should be and looked the other way. Coats hung alongside scoreboards nailed to a line of trees only just beginning to sprout after their spring pollarding. The audience sitting on the red hardwood benches was mostly made up of taxi-drivers waiting for the arrival of the next train from Bordeaux.

Monsieur Pamplemousse joined them, watching first one game, then the other, but he found it hard to concentrate and after a moment or two he continued with his walk.

Something untoward was going on at the Hôtel des Dunes, that was for sure. The Super hadn't said it in so many words, but at one point – either by accident or design – he'd let slip the fact that it had been under observation prior to the murder. He didn't say why or for how long.

At the end of the parking area Monsieur Pamplemousse made his way back to the pavement and stood waiting for the traffic lights to change before crossing the road. As he did so he happened to glance across towards the far side of the busy square. To his surprise he saw Elsie coming out of the post office on the corner.

Wearing a striped Breton jersey over matching dark-blue slacks and yachting cap, she looked the picture of health. She might well have just stepped out of a commercial advertising the life-giving powers of ozone. Heads turned as she disappeared in the direction of the sea, her high heels giving her bottom a decidedly provocative wiggle.

Monsieur Pamplemousse had to admit that his feeling of relief at seeing Elsie was tinged with guilt. His first reaction when she hadn't responded to his knock at breakfast time had been one of panic that he'd done nothing to follow up the Director's telephone call and that something might have happened to her. A hurried check of the rack in the hall had shown that her room key was missing, as was a note he'd left saying he had to leave early and suggesting they meet outside the casino later that morning, so that they could inspect another restaurant at lunch time.

Elsie certainly didn't look as though she'd spent the night in debauchery; quite the reverse. Most likely she had slept late and then got a taxi into Arcachon. Either that or someone had given her a lift. As for being in the *P.T.T.*, she had probably been doing nothing more mysterious than posting a card to Reginald.

The thought reminded Monsieur Pamplemousse that he hadn't sent a card to Doucette. It was usually the first thing he did. Following Elsie down avenue Gambetta he stopped outside a *tabac* and found himself confronted by what at first sight seemed like an embarrassment of riches, but which he quickly narrowed down to a choice between shots of the dunes taken from a variety of angles, the oyster beds at high tide, the same oyster beds six hours later, a distant view of the lighthouse at Cap Ferret taken from the Arcachon side of the bay, the tapping of pine trees for their resin – the second local industry – or what looked like the same nude girl disporting herself on one of the many sheltered beaches round the bay. He decided to play safe with a montage of the first five.

While he was in the shop he bought a map and a local guide to the area in order to top up on his store of information. *Le Guide* concentrated on hotels and restaurants. Details concerning the area itself were kept as succinct as possible and there was always something new to learn.

As he waited for his change, Monsieur Pamplemousse glanced at the headlines in some of the *journaux*. Most of them accorded space on the front page to the disappearance of Monsieur Bouet, but there was no mention of foul play, nor of the possibility of there being a second body. The Police must be playing it down for all they were worth. He wondered why. Perhaps they thought it would be bad for the tourist trade just prior to the season.

After making his way through the town he stopped on the front to admire an old double-tiered carousel. The organ music cheered him up a little and he wandered on to the pier to

watch the local fishermen angling for their evening meal. He
wished now he'd suggested meeting Elsie earlier. She was
probably doing a round of the boutiques.

A yellow bulldozer went about its task of levelling the
beach. A low-flying Air Force jet shot past making everyone
jump.

As he left the pier a coach drew up and began disgorging a load of elderly passengers. Some set off immediately
to join a queue for the nearby Aquarium, others sat down
on the nearest bench, seeking the shade of the tamarisk
trees which lined the promenade; the more adventurous
made their way down on to the beach, the men removing their
shoes and socks and rolling up their trousers as they entered
the sea, the women abandoning all sense of propriety as they
lifted their skirts in a way they would never have done at
home.

Truffert was right. Water did something to people. He should
know. Before becoming an Inspector he'd spent years in the
Merchant Navy. It was such a sparkling day Monsieur Pamplemousse was almost tempted to join them. Doucette would
have been in there like a shot.

Pommes Frites had no inhibitions. There were shrieks and
cries of 'Ooh, la! la!' as he dashed into the water.

Monsieur Pamplemousse fitted a wide angle lens to his
Leica and recorded the moment for posterity.

Looking at the scene through the view-finder it was hard to
believe that only a short while before, and a bare kilometre or
so away at that, those same waters had witnessed what had
every appearance of being not one, but two particularly bloody
murders. He wondered what the reaction would be if a leg or
an arm suddenly floated into view, or if one of the fishermen
hooked something unexpected. It would certainly put them off
their *dîner*.

Feeling at a loose end, he worked his way along the beach, pausing every so often in order to throw a stick for Pommes Frites. Reaching some concrete steps, he climbed them slowly and found himself standing on the outer wall of a vast marina. It was a forest of masts; packed with yachts and motor craft of every shape and kind – there must be two thousand at least. To his left, at the entrance to the harbour, a statue in the shape of a giant anchor was dedicated to those lost at sea; a warning to week-end sailors who must go past it in droves during the season, although if the speed at which most of the current ones were travelling was anything to go by he doubted if many of them gave it a second glance. Time and a desire to be first in the queue took priority.

He was about to take another photograph when he heard his name being called. Panning quickly down he registered a familiar figure waving to him from the stern of a motor launch just leaving the marina.

Elsie, her blonde hair streaming in the wind, had discarded her trousers and top in favour of a minuscule black bikini. It struck Monsieur Pamplemousse that as she hadn't been carrying a beach bag she must have come prepared. He clicked the shutter before returning her wave.

As the boat swept past he recognised one of the Americans at the helm; the oldest of the three and the one who seemed to be the leader. The other two were nowhere to be seen. Perhaps they were still in the casino.

Daylight did nothing for him; sunlight even less. He would have been more at home on the lower slopes of Montmartre than here in Arcachon. Despite his expensive clothes and shoes you could see your face in, he was surprised Elsie didn't see him for what he was – a *voyou* – a hoodlum. There was no accounting for tastes.

Rapidly changing to a narrow angle lens, Monsieur Pamplemousse followed the boat's progress as it passed through the harbour entrance and made a turn to port. It looked as though Elsie and her new-found escort were heading towards the furthest tip of the peninsula at the entrance to the bay.

Monsieur Pamplemousse's first impulse was to ignore the whole thing. Write it off as being all part of life's rich, and sometimes most unsatisfactory pattern. What did it matter to him if Elsie had chosen to ignore his note? If she was prepared to risk chalking up a black mark that was her decision.

All the same, he couldn't help feeling intrigued.

A moment later, acting on an impulse, he made his way quickly back along the beach in the direction of the pier. He was in luck's way. The 11.30 ferry to Cap Ferret was about to leave. Signalling Pommes Frites to go first, he scrambled after him and made his way through the crowded cabin towards the open stern. They had the last two seats.

Seconds later the boat slipped its moorings and edged out from the steps. As soon as it was clear of the pier, it swung round in a wide circle between two rows of marker buoys and then quickly gathered speed.

Heading south, they hugged the coast for a while, past rows of small hotels and apartment blocks interspersed with occasional examples of baroque housing: a hotch-potch of sea-side architecture.

Pyla-sur-Mer came into view and as soon as they were clear of the oyster beds the boat swung to starboard and headed west towards the far side of the bay.

Looking back over his shoulder, Monsieur Pamplemousse had a clear view of the dune. At the Arcachon end a zig-zag vertical line of enormous old wartime pill-boxes lay at drunken angles. Was it his imagination working overtime, or did they have a certain doom-laden air about them? Although they had obviously shifted their position over the years, they were so solid, nothing short of an atom bomb would ever destroy them completely. They had been built to last for ever; part of an unfulfilled plan by the Germans during the war to transform the Basin into a haven for their fleet of warships. Making use of his camera lens again he made out a helicopter landing-pad on a jetty to the town side of the beach. To its right there was a First Aid station with a red cross painted on its roof. From the look of the water level the tide must be around the halfway mark. Panning up, he searched in vain for the hotel, but it was hidden by the trees.

It was hard to picture the possibility that somewhere in that vast mass of sand lay the grizzly remains of the hotel *patron*. If it were true, then they might never be found. It was no wonder the police had given up; it was a thankless task.

Monsieur Pamplemousse gave an involuntary shiver. He couldn't have put it into words, but neither could he escape the feeling that somehow the forces of fate were beginning to take over. It was the age-old question of what made you be in a certain place at a certain time. Was it pure chance that led him to be sitting where he was at that particular moment? If he had waited until the next ferry, or spent time writing his card to Doucette, would everything from that moment on be different? He would never know the answer.

It was hard to raise any feelings for someone he hadn't met; he didn't even have the remotest idea what Monsieur Bouet had looked like. All the same, Monsieur Pamplemousse couldn't help wondering what he had done to end up the way he had. If he'd upset someone then he must have done it in a big way. Perhaps, if he had a guilty secret, he'd carried it with him to his sandy grave. And what about his assistant? Had he been a party to the same secret, or had he accidentally stumbled across something he shouldn't have?

Madame Bouet was obviously taking it badly, as well she might. Nevertheless, someone would have to run the hotel. If the first night's performance was anything to go by they would need a new chef for a start.

Not for the first time he found himself toying with the idea of looking elsewhere. The German couple had already left. Perhaps even now they were having another row in a shower further along the coast. But Elsie seemed dead set on staying put and at least his room was reasonably comfortable.

Monsieur Pamplemousse scanned the water for any sign of her boat, but the bay was busy with craft of all shapes and sizes – a mixture of yachts and motor launches, with here and there a larger boat carrying a party out for a day's fishing.

To be totally truthful he had to admit to more than a faint twinge of jealousy that Elsie had left him in the lurch, totally ignoring his note. He couldn't even console himself that it was for a younger man; that he could have well understood. It was simply someone with the means to hire a boat. And why not? Perhaps because for all Elsie's faults he'd thought better of her. She didn't have to say yes to the first man who came along. Clearly she had made a play for more than a turn of the wheel at the casino last night. He wondered what Reginald would have to say if he got to hear of it.

Monsieur Pamplemousse felt more and more aggrieved. Elsie wasn't exactly proving to be a dedicated representative of Le Guide. There had been no question of her asking if she could have the day off. Normally she would have been expected to explore the area, checking on other entries in Le Guide, making notes on any changes which might have taken place. It all had to go down.

Pulling his hat down over his face to shield it from the sun, he settled back to make himself comfortable. He should have known better. It was a signal for the boatman to throttle back. Yet more oyster beds came into view and a moment later they slid alongside the pier at Bélisaire. It was almost mid-day. The journey had taken just over twenty minutes.

Monsieur Pamplemousse hesitated outside a café at the end of the pier, but it was too early for lunch. A narrow-gauge railway track ran along the side of the road. It disappeared invitingly round a corner and into some woods, but the tiny platform by the terminus was deserted. He consulted a time-table on the wall of the booking office. The first train wasn't due to leave until the afternoon so, with Pommes Frites at his heels, he set off to explore the area on foot.

Large private houses built at a time when the area was the summer haunt of wealthy burghers from Bordeaux rubbed shoulders with modern apartment blocks now occupied by lesser mortals. Cars with boat trailers proliferated.

Their walk took them back down a pedestrian precinct lined with identical eating places displaying carbon-copy menus. There was a smell of cheap cooking oil in the air. Elsie was nowhere to be seen.

Lost in thought, Monsieur Pamplemousse gave a jump as there was a sudden sharp crack from behind him. He ducked instinctively, only to see a small boy on a skateboard shoot past, weaving his way in and out of the other pedestrians before executing some complicated airborne manoeuvre which doubtless had some esoteric name – like a banana or a porcupine. There was another, louder crack as he landed heavily on the paving stones. A strange variation – half skate-board, half uni-cycle – came out of a side street. It was pro-pelled with great aplomb by its owner. A moment later both boys disappeared down the precinct without a word being ex-changed.

Monsieur Pamplemousse envied their style and self-confidence. In his time it had been roller skates – not very good ones at that – and he'd had to run the gauntlet of running comments from his contemporaries. Nowadays, communication other than by means of monosyllabic grunts seemed almost a sign of weakness.

He returned to the harbour feeling hungry after the walk. The café by the pier was beginning to fill up. He studied the menu outside, comparing it with what was on the plates of those already eating. Taste buds signalled their approval.

Finding himself one of the few remaining tables near the water's edge, he sat back to admire the view. It was easy to see why it was so popular with the purveyors of postcards.

The little harbour was surrounded by oyster beds, misshapen branches sticking vertically from the water to mark the perimeter gave them a kind of rustic charm. The layers of flat plastic mesh baskets containing the oysters in the second stage of their development piled up in long rows. When the tide came in they would disappear again. Nature, according to the guide book, ensured that their water was changed twice a day; 400 million cubic metres of it. The annual oyster production in the bay of Arcachon was between ten and twelve thousand tonnes; 37,000 acres out of a total area of 4,320,000 was given over to it.

In the face of such statistics Monsieur Pamplemousse had no choice but to order a sea-food platter and a *demi* Muscadet. Detecting a certain restiveness below the table, he asked for a *steak frites* and a *pichet* of *vin rouge* to follow.

Beyond the oyster beds he could see a few motor launches at anchor in the water, but it was impossible to tell which, if any, might be the one Elsie had been in. From a distance they all looked the same. It was quite possible her escort had tied up in one of the little harbours further along the coast at the far end of the Cap. If, indeed, they had come to that end of the peninsula at all. There were plenty of alternative places dotted along the coast.

The sea-food platter came and went, and while the paraphernalia of plate stand, dishes and other impedimenta were being removed, Monsieur Pamplemousse dipped his fingers in a bowl of water, wiped them dry with his napkin, then poured himself some more wine and settled back to await the arrival of the steak. He was beginning to feel more at peace with the world. The only cloud on an otherwise spotless horizon came in the form of a warning growl from somewhere near his feet.

Looking around, Monsieur Pamplemousse realised why. It was a question of territories. Pommes Frites was having to compete with the regulars; a motley selection of resident freelancers who obviously put in a daily appearance. In a brief survey of the surrounding tables he counted no less than nine other dogs. Apart from a Dandie Dinmont and what in a poor light might have passed for a Dogue de Bordeaux, they were a raggle-taggle selection of ambiguous pedigree and even more uncertain ancestry.

Doubtless encouraged by residents with an eye to saving on biscuits during the holiday season, they patrolled the restaurant with an expert air, sizing up the clientèle before homing in on likely looking subjects. Once a decision had been made they settled down as close as possible to their chosen target, watching every mouthful. A mangy-looking Wolfhound with unusually yellow teeth appeared to be the ring-leader. Definitely not a dog to be trifled with. Not that it appeared to bother Pommes Frites. A visiting Chihuahua belonging to a woman at the next table looked suitably grateful as yet another growl sent the animal packing.

As his second course arrived, Monsieur Pamplemousse

reached for the mustard and resolutely turned his back on the scene.

The steak, lightly seared under the grill, was covered in melted butter. The *frites* arrived seconds later, piping hot on a separate platter. He tested one in his fingers. It was as he liked them, crisp and golden on the outside, yet soft and yielding within. In the end it was the simple dishes he enjoyed the most, although they were often the hardest to do. Pommes Frites stirred expectantly as he heard his master call for a green salad. It was a good sign.

It was as Monsieur Pamplemousse cut and speared the first mouthful of his steak that he happened to catch sight of another ferry arriving. He glanced at his watch. It must be the 14.30 from Arcachon. The light was perfect. Only the waves from the wake of the boat as it swung round to tie up below the end of the pier disturbed the reflections in the water. Reaching for his camera, he quickly composed a picture of the jetty with the oyster beds in the background. Foreground interest was provided by a potted shrub, one of a row standing outside the restaurant.

Having waited patiently for the *moment critique* when the passengers were halfway through disembarking, Monsieur Pamplemousse was about to press the shutter release button when he froze. To his horror, slap bang in the middle of the picture he saw Monsieur and Madame Blanche advancing down the pier. There was no possibility of escape. They were heading straight towards him. Recognition on their part was but a few short steps away.

Afterwards Monsieur Pamplemousse couldn't remember exactly what came over him. Perhaps it was simply a case of desperate situations demanding desperate but not necessarily considered measures. Whatever the reasoning, or lack of reasoning behind it, having issued a peremptory order to

Pommes Frites to make himself scarce with all possible speed, he made a grab for the Chihuahua at the next table and with his other hand reached out towards his plate. The blissful expression on the creature's face as it caught sight of an approaching meal faded rapidly as its tongue, wet with anticipation, made contact with the steak.

All major events need some train of events to set them going. The atomic bomb requires its minor explosion to trigger off the horrifying chain reaction; earthquakes come about because of movement within the bowels of the earth which eventually cause them to erupt in protest. In the case of the Chihuahua it was the unexpected advent of *moutarde de Dijon* against tongue which provided the necessary catalyst.

Although he had never been lucky enough to witness a performance at the *Comédie française*, let alone the *Théâtre nationale* (even at matinée performances neither establishment exactly went out of its way to encourage the presence of *chiens*), Pommes Frites considered himself something of a connoisseur when it came to the raw material of life from which writers of plays gained their ideas.

Having stationed himself behind a convenient tree at what he judged to be a suitably safe distance from both Monsieur Pamplemousse and the restaurant, he watched in silent awe as the drama before him unfolded with alarming speed. The aggrieved expression on his face at having been banished from the table changed to one of wonder. Everywhere he looked there was something fresh to be seen.

Waiters, who until that moment had resolutely refused to catch the eye of diners impatient for their *l'addition,* appeared as if by magic. The chef materialised brandishing a carving knife. He was followed by a bevy of lesser hands, each clutching an implement of their particular calling; oyster knives vied with glass decanters, meat pounders with butcher's cleavers. The sound effects were deafening. It was theatre in the round and no mistake.

In the centre of it all the Chihuahua, foaming at the mouth, its eyes as large as saucers and as red as the proverbial beet-root, took one terrified look at what was going on around it, then made a dive inside Monsieur Pamplemousse's jacket where it proceeded to part company with the steak, noisily and with all possible speed.

Taking full advantage of the diversion, and emboldened by the absence of Pommes Frites, the Wolfhound rallied his troops with a brief but pointed howl, then led them in clearing un-watched plates of their contents. Bellows of rage and feminine shrieks rose from all sides. In a matter of seconds the restau-rant became a seething mass of snarling fur.

The owner of the Chihuahua, distraught at seeing the state its loved one was in as it emerged gasping for air from the confines of Monsieur Pamplemousse's jacket, climbed on to a chair and began crossing herself as though her own end was also nigh. Downing the last of his wine, a priest at an adjoin-ing table hastened to provide comfort. He looked all set to perform the final rites.

If the object of the exercise had been to divert Monsieur and Madame Blanche's attention from any possible relation-ship between himself and Pommes Frites, Monsieur Pam-plemousse had succeeded beyond his wildest dreams.

Even from a distance of some fifty paces it needed no expert in lip-reading to perceive Madame Blanche's views on the matter. The oval shape formed by her lips said it all. It was a 'poof' to end all 'poofs'. The look of scorn on her face as she went on her way dragging Monsieur Blanche behind her was something to behold. Pommes Frites shrank back behind the tree, holding his breath until they were safely past.

When he next looked out he saw to his disappointment that

the pageant was nearing its end. He was just in time to see his master disappearing down the road with the Wolfhound loping along behind. If Monsieur Pamplemousse had every appearance of making a bid for the next Olympics, the dog was behaving as though it had all the time in the world. It even paused for a moment in order to take a quick snatch from a clump of grass. Only the sight of its bared teeth and the sound of a scarcely suppressed snarl pointed to the fact that, far from being a vegetarian, it was merely working up an appetite before going in for the kill.

Pommes Frites gave a sigh as he set off after them. He was too nice a dog to spend overlong on the thought that it served his master right, but as both hunted and hunter disappeared round a corner, he couldn't help but dwell on it for a moment or two, wondering if perhaps the full moon were responsible for his master's strange behaviour over the past few days.

Thoughts of a philosophical nature were far from Monsieur Pamplemousse's mind as he raced through the town. They ranged from wondering what would happen if he took refuge in a passing gift shop – the owners were hardly likely to welcome him with open arms – to weighing up his chances of escape by plunging down a side street and into the sea. Clearly, from the way they were shying away he would get little or no help from any of the passers-by. No one would come to his rescue if the dog turned out to be a powerful swimmer.

In the end the solution rose up in front of him in the shape of a tall, white cigar-shaped building, the red top of which was surmounted by a glass enclosure.

Summoning up a final burst of speed which took even the Wolfhound by surprise, he beat it to the lighthouse by several yards.

Ignoring an elderly woman in black seated behind a desk

in the entrance hall, cutting off in its prime her explanation that although there was no entrance charge, *pourboires* were at the discretion of the individual and would benefit those prepared at any time of the day or night to drop what they were doing in order to risk their lives in ensuring the safety of others – it was up to *Monsieur* – he made for the stairs, leaving her saucer of carefully arranged ten-franc coins undisturbed.

Had he paused to consult his guide, Monsieur Pamplemousse would have seen in passing that there were 258 steps to the top of the lighthouse. He didn't bother to count, but if pressed he would have put it at many more.

Emerging on to the viewing platform at long last, he collapsed against the perimeter wall, fighting to regain his breath. Focusing his gaze on the ground some fifty metres below he could see no sign of the Wolfhound. Either the brute had given up the chase or it was already on its way up. With any luck it had fallen foul of the *Madame* at the door.

Gradually he became aware that he was not alone. On the other side of the circular platform he could hear voices. Peering round the corner he saw a small group of sightseers being regaled by an ancient mariner on the splendour of the panoramic view spread out before them. If they had witnessed his ignominious progress through the town they showed no sign. Most of them seemed more interested in the local football stadium.

The man was making the most of his captive audience.

'*Oui.* There is nothing between us and the United States of America. Just five thousand or so kilometres of Atlantic Ocean.

'*Oui, oui.* In winter the storms can be very bad. Last winter they were the worst we had ever known. The whole lighthouse swayed. You see the *Limite de Prudence* . . .' he pointed to a line of white-capped rollers between the two strips of land marking the point where the sea entered the bay. 'That was one mass of boiling water. The Dune du Pilat . . .' heads turned in Monsieur Pamplemousse's direction, 'the Dune du Pilat was like the Sahara desert in the middle of a sandstorm.

'*Non.* The white tower you can see a kilometre and a half away to the west was not the original lighthouse. This,' said with some pride, 'this is the site of the original. It has always been so. The lighthouse may have been destroyed by the Germans in 1944, but in 1946 it was completely rebuilt.

'The white building is the Semaphore Tower . . . it is used by the military. That has always been there – for as long as I can remember. The new lighthouse was built on exactly the same spot as the old.'

Monsieur Pamplemousse listened with only half an ear. The other half was waiting for the sound of approaching paws.

'*Oui.*' The man turned in response to a question. 'The restaurant by the harbour is a good place to eat.'

'That is true. I have just eaten there myself.' Even as he spoke Monsieur Pamplemousse realised he had made a mistake. The warm sun combined with his marathon sprint through the town had left their mark. A malodorous smell was beginning to emanate from his person.

The keeper stared at him for a brief moment or two, then turned. The others hastily followed on behind as he moved away towards the leeward side of the building.

'From here you can see the whole of the Fôret Domaniele de Lège et Garonne . . .' But the damage was done. The attention of his audience was concentrated instead on Monsieur Pamplemousse. Mostly it was one of alarm as he followed them round the circular platform. In an effort to escape several tried to push their way past him towards the stairs, then clearly wished they hadn't as he barred their progress.

Monsieur Pamplemousse was trying to keep his options open. The worst was about to happen. His ears had picked up the sound of heavy breathing. It was getting louder with every passing second.

It was a fifty-fifty chance which way the animal went. If it turned right at the top he was done for; if it turned left it would have to push its way through the crowd and time would be on his side. To Monsieur Pamplemousse's relief he heard it turn left.

Taking advantage of the sudden diversion he made a dive through the opening and disappeared down the stairs rather faster than he had come up. A moment later he set off down the road, this time taking a different direction, away from the Bay side and towards the Atlantic ocean.

Monsieur Pamplemousse's sudden flight didn't go unnoticed. Resting his chin on the parapet of the observation platform, Pommes Frites watched in amazement as act two of the drama in mime unfolded before his very eyes.

His master appeared to have gone berserk. Having overtaken a small boy on a skateboard, he suddenly stopped, turned, and entered into conversation with him. First came the crouching down and the patting of the head. Then, when that seemed to be of no avail, it was followed by the old trick of distracting attention. Monsieur Pamplemousse pointed up to an imaginary object in the sky and while the boy's back was turned he made a grab for the skateboard.

It must have been something of a desperate measure, for he only travelled a matter of a few metres before he fell off. Rising to his feet and dusting himself down, he then ran hither and thither for a while, before making a wild dash for a small train winding its way up from the beach. He appeared to be having an argument, first with the driver, then with the passengers as he clung to the side trying to force his way in to the crowded carriage.

Eventually, as the train slowed down for some traffic lights, he leapt off it and began waving at some distant figures walking away from him up the road – they were too far away for Pommes Frites to recognise them – but clearly his master knew who they were.

Then, almost as though he'd had a sudden change of mind and didn't want to see them after all, he hid behind a tree until they had disappeared down a lane leading towards the sea.

Pommes Frites shook his head sadly as he followed Monsieur Pamplemousse's progress from tree to tree until he was but a speck on the horizon. He had a friend in Paris whose owner had behaved in a similar fashion. In the end he'd had to be taken away. He didn't know what he would do if that happened.

Having decided the time had come for him to intervene, Pommes Frites made a firm mental note of the point where he had last seen his master, then set off in pursuit.

Unaware of the consternation he had been causing, Monsieur Pamplemousse relaxed for the first time since he'd fled from the café. The Wolfhound must have given up the chase for it was nowhere to be seen. But best of all he had found what he was looking for. There in the firm sand near the water's edge he'd come across two sets of footprints. One set looked as though they had been made by a pair of rope-soled boating shoes; the other had to be Elsie's. There couldn't be many people on the beach that day who were wearing high heels.

He quickened his pace. The tide was coming in fast. It wouldn't be long before all traces disappeared completely.

It wasn't until he rounded a groyne and looked up that Monsieur Pamplemousse suddenly realised he had been so busy following the footprints he had completely lost sight of his immediate surroundings. As far as the eye could see there were naked bodies stretched out on the sand: hectares and hectares of bare flesh in various shades of pink, brown and black. Several of those nearest to him were already giving him strange looks as they caught sight of his camera. There was a very definite feeling of unrest in the air. The man nearest to him reached for a portable telephone.

Monsieur Pamplemousse beat a hasty retreat and made his way up the beach in the direction of a small dune. To his relief there was no one else in sight – probably because his side of the groyne was exposed to the prevailing wind. He weighed up the pros and cons of the situation for a moment or two. The possibility that Elsie and her escort might be making for one of the many nudist beaches dotted along the Atlantic coast hadn't crossed his mind. It put him on the horns of a dilemma and no mistake.

There was only one thing for it. Crouching down, he divested himself of his clothing. Folding it into a neat pile, he placed it on a patch of dry sand well out of reach of the incoming tide. Then, pulling the brim of his hat down over his eyes, he lengthened the straps on his camera case, slung it round his front and, with the nonchalant air of one who did such things every day of his life, retraced his steps.

Keeping as close to the water's edge as possible, his only other article of adornment – a gold Capillard-Rieme wristwatch – glinting in the afternoon sun, Monsieur Pamplemousse resumed the pursuit of his quarry, adding his not inconsiderable mite of whiteness to the general ambience.

It was some ten minutes later, having followed a course roughly identical to that of his master, that Pommes Frites arrived on the scene. It was no great feat of navigation.

Indeed, it would have needed a hound with singularly insensitive nostrils not to have located where Monsieur Pamplemousse had ended up. Pommes Frites could have done it with his eyes closed.

At first his joy at finding the clothes had been unbounded, alloyed only by a faint feeling of puzzlement as to why his master wasn't inside them. Never one to harbour a grudge, ever ready to turn the other jowl, he followed the trail of footprints down the beach as far as the water's edge. There he stopped dead in his tracks, scanning the water in vain, for there wasn't a soul to be seen. Suddenly he feared the worst. On his way there he had seen a red flag flying. Even Pommes Frites knew that a red flag meant danger. He let out a howl.

The thought that Monsieur Pamplemousse might have gone swimming for pleasure never entered his mind. In all the time he had known him he had never seen Monsieur Pamplemousse don a bathing costume let alone enter the water. There was only one interpretation to be arrived at. The answer was simple. Something had snapped and his master had decided to end it all.

Pommes Frites made his way back up the beach with a heavy heart. There was only one thing to be done. It was a case of carrying out the canine equivalent of a burial at sea. And as with a burial at sea, when the waters close inexorably over the coffin and it disappears without a trace, so, having dragged his master's clothes back down the beach and dug a suitably large hole, he paid his last respects as an extra large wave broke over the spot.

Barring an earthquake or some other act of God, Pommes Frites felt confident that Monsieur Pamplemousse's belongings would remain undisturbed until the end of time. No bone could have been better hidden, no tribute more sincere. It was a simple gesture, but in the circumstances it was the least a dog could do for his master.

7
POMMES FRITES
THINKS AGAIN

Monsieur Pamplemousse gazed at the spot where he was perfectly certain he had left his clothes less than a quarter of an hour before. 'I can assure you they were here. I remember the place exactly. There is the rock . . . there is a piece of sea-weed . . .'

'*Oui, Monsieur*.' The *gendarme* sounded weary.

'It is a *mystère*.'

'*Oui, Monsieur*. Perhaps they have been stolen?'

Monsieur Pamplemousse looked around the beach. There wasn't a soul in sight on their side of the groyne. He gave the sand a desultory stab with his toe. It felt soft and yielding.

'No one in their right mind would have taken them. They are covered in *chien*'s vomit.'

The *gendarme* gave a shrug. Clearly the state of Monsieur Pamplemousse's clothes was of academic interest beside the matter in hand.

'There have been a number of complaints, *Monsieur*. From those on the *plage des naturistes*, you understand?'

Monsieur Pamplemousse raised himself to his full height. 'Are you accusing me of being a voyeur?' he thundered. '*Un individu qui se rince l'oeil*? – a peeping Tom?'

Wilting beneath his gaze, the *gendarme* lowered his eyes.

He contemplated Monsieur Pamplemousse's lower regions for a moment or two, then took out his notebook.

While the man was busy writing, Monsieur Pamplemousse took the opportunity to lengthen his camera strap still further.

'I am an ornithologist.'

The *gendarme* gave a sigh. 'That is what they all say, *Monsieur*. But with respect, I would suggest *Monsieur* is looking in the wrong direction. The Ile aux Oiseaux is on the other side of the peninsula. It is inside the Bassin d'Arcachon.'

'I am perfectly well aware of that,' said Monsieur Pamplemousse. 'I happen to be looking for the Banc d'Arguin which is at the entrance to the Bassin. I understand it is covered with marram grass and that it provides shelter for a large colony of seabirds. I am particularly interested in the sandwich tern.'

The *gendarme* carried on writing. 'I am pleased to see *Monsieur* has made good use of our local guide. Doubtless *Monsieur* has his camera with him because of his interest in bird watching.'

The *double entendre* did not go unnoticed by Monsieur Pamplemousse. He decided he must tread carefully and try not to lose his temper.

'May I see your *carte d'identité, Monsieur*?'

'Oh, *Mon Dieu! Mon Dieu!*' Monsieur Pamplemousse made a great play of patting himself all over, first both sides of his chest, then his hips and finally his posterior. 'I had it with me when I came out this morning. I wonder where it can possibly be?'

The truth of the matter – in fact the only ray of sunshine in the whole dismal affair – was that in anticipation of his being asked that very same question when he visited the *gendarmerie* in Arcachon he had changed into his other suit. His precious notebook in the secret compartment of his right trouser leg, his Cross pen without which he always felt lost, his identity card and various other personal items he would have been sad to lose, were all safely tucked away in the hotel room.

His attempt at striking a jovial note failed miserably. Clearly it had had the opposite effect. Officialdom came into play.

'In that case, *Monsieur*, I must ask you to accompany me to the *commissariat de police*.'

'I trust you have some kind of covering in your *voiture*.' Monsieur Pamplemousse followed the *gendarme* up the beach. 'A blanket perhaps? Or even a rug?'

The man gave a hollow laugh. 'This is not Paris, *Monsieur*. It is not even Bordeaux.' He pointed to a bicycle propped against a tree.

Monsieur Pamplemousse stared at it. 'You mean I am to ride that!'

'No, *Monsieur*,' said the *gendarme* patiently. 'I shall be riding the *bicyclette*. You will be walking.'

'Walking? How far is the *gendarmerie*?'

'How far?' The question gave rise to a certain amount of head scratching. 'The nearest one is at Le Petit Piquet. Nine kilometres away . . . perhaps ten. I am only on attachment for the day. It is the start of the holiday season and . . .'

'*Je refuse! Absolument!*'

The *gendarme* leaned over his handlebars and peered at Monsieur Pamplemousse's watch. 'There is always the *autobus* if you prefer it. If we hurry we may just catch the next one to Bordeaux.'

'No, I would not prefer it!' barked Monsieur Pamplemousse.

The *gendarme* shrugged. 'As you wish, *Monsieur*. In that case I will leave you here while I telephone for assistance.' He cocked his head in the direction of the next beach. 'By the sound of it you will not be alone.'

Monsieur Pamplemousse gave a start. He'd been so engrossed in his own misfortunes he had failed to pay any attention to what was going on around him. Now that the gendarme mentioned it there did seem to be an inordinate amount of noise coming from the other side of the groyne. Screams, shouts, voices raised in anger; it sounded for all the world as though someone was holding a lynching party.

He essayed a quick peep over the top.

'*Sacré bleu!*'

'*Monsieur?*' The officer joined him. '*Mon dieu! Chiens!*'

Monsieur Pamplemousse sank down out of sight. If he hadn't seen it with his own eyes he wouldn't have believed it possible.

It wasn't just *chiens*, it was one particular *chien*. What Pommes Frites thought he was up to was hard to imagine. Or rather – he rephrased the question – what he was up to was clear for all to see. Why he was doing it was another matter entirely.

Not to put too fine a point on it, and for reasons best known to himself, Pommes Frites was busily engaged in running up and down the beach sniffing all and sundry as fast as he could go. As an exercise in the triggering-off of girlish screams and manly oaths it was highly successful. One touch of his wet nose on an unsuspecting *derrière* and the effect was both instantaneous and electric. But as a means of endearing himself to the population at large it ranked as a non-starter. The *plage* was in an uproar.

'Is there nowhere else we can go?' demanded Monsieur Pamplemousse. 'You cannot possibly expect me to walk nine kilometres like this.'

The *gendarme* considered the matter. 'The *Mairie* in Bélisaire is not far away,' he said dubiously.

'Then I suggest we make our way there with all possible

speed,' said Monsieur Pamplemousse.

'I will take your camera, *Monsieur*.'

'Is that necessary?'

'I am afraid so, *Monsieur*.' The *gendarme* didn't actually say it might be used in evidence against him, but Monsieur Pamplemousse got the point.

'May I suggest *Monsieur* makes use of his *chapeau* instead?'

Monsieur Pamplemousse hastily swopped his hat for the camera.

The *gendarme* gave a whistle as he took it. 'An R4. This is some camera.' He fondled it with his hands. 'Lovely finish. You get what you pay for, I suppose. I don't think I'd want to take it on the beach. One grain of sand and . . .'

'You are interested in photography?'

'A little. But nothing like this. This is what I call a professional job.' He checked the number of exposures taken, then held the camera up to his eye. 'I see you are using a wide-angle lens, *Monsieur*.'

'I was just taking some general views,' said Monsieur Pamplemousse. 'To establish the geography.'

'Aaah !'

'*Merde!*' Monsieur Pamplemousse suddenly realised his other lens had been in his trouser pocket.

'There is something wrong, *Monsieur*?'

'It is nothing,' said Monsieur Pamplemousse. Nothing! Nearly four thousand francs worth of lens. Madame Grante would not be amused.

He glanced anxiously over his shoulder as more shrieks came from the next beach. The worst possible scenario would be if he was linked in any way with what was happening on the other side of the groyne. That, coming on top of everything else, would be the final straw.

There was a click. 'Nice shutter, too,' said the gendarme. 'Very easy movement. Lovely camera.'

'I do wish you wouldn't point it in my direction,' said Monsieur Pamplemousse crossly.

Glancing anxiously over his shoulder in case Pommes Frites caught sight of him walking off the beach, Monsieur Pamplemousse followed the *gendarme* along a slatted wooden walkway leading towards the main road.

He needn't have worried. Pommes Frites' mind was on other things. Sensing the moment of truth had arrived, glad to be of service at long last, he was in his element as he darted hither and thither, sniffing a bottom here, checking another one there. Not since the passing out party at the end of his course with the Paris Sûreté had he been able to give such free rein to his natural instincts without fear of repercussions from on high.

After burying his master's clothing, he had spent some time turning the whole matter over in his mind. Although blessed with lightning reactions in an emergency, Pommes Frites' thought processes were not always of the fastest. Not for him the snap decisions of a business tycoon; fax machines requiring instant replies would have had short shrift in his kennel; computer salesmen would have been shown the door.

Following a great deal of long-drawn-out reasoning, which he had carried out while exploring the hinterland of Bélisaire, he had begun to wonder if he had done the right thing. Once the seeds of doubt had been sown they had grown rapidly.

It struck him for a start that if Monsieur Pamplemousse had done away with himself he wouldn't have taken his camera with him. Nor would he have carried out the deed wearing a hat. Monsieur Pamplemousse was very punctilious about that sort of thing. Whichever way he looked at it, from whatever angle, Pommes Frites reached the inescapable conclusion that he'd made a boo boo. There was a distinct possibility his master might not have given up the ghost after all.

It was with such thoughts uppermost in his mind that he returned to the beach only to discover the tide had come in a long way during his rambles. It was while swimming ashore after a fruitless search of the sea bed for his burial ground that he came across the beach full of nudists and hope of finding his master alive and well was born again.

The first bad news for Monsieur Pamplemousse during his walk to the *Mairie* came in the shape of a black diesel-engined locomotive belonging to the *Tramways du Cap Ferret*. It was on top of them before he had a chance to hide. With a shriek of protesting metal, the engine rounded a bend pulling behind it three open-sided carriages packed with holiday-makers wending their way home from the beach. The driver gave a toot, and as the whole entourage ground to a halt he leaned out of his cab and exchanged a brief word with the *gendarme*. Another note was added to the latter's book.

To Monsieur Pamplemousse's horror he caught sight of Elsie and her companion sitting in the last carriage. Fortunately he spotted them first, but it was a narrow squeak. He did the only thing possible. To avoid recognition he covered his face with his hat.

As the train rattled on its way several of the passengers applauded, but by then Monsieur Pamplemousse was past caring.

Still bothered by the event, he was ill-prepared for the second encounter. It happened when they reached the shopping mall. The mother of the skate-boarding child was waiting for him. She pursued him down the road pointing an accusing finger and hurling abuse. Seeing Monsieur Pamplemousse in a state of *déshabillé* clearly confirmed her worst suspicions. Others joined in, until what had started off as a purely personal vendetta grew out of all proportion.

The very, very bad news came as they neared the *Mairie*; an unlikely modern building not far from the lighthouse. Signs outside advertised an exhibition by local artists. Either they were small in number or space was at a premium. Monsieur Pamplemousse had never seen such a small *mairie*. As he followed the *gendarme* up the drive, tempering haste to escape the throng with as much dignity as he could muster in the circumstances, he nearly collided with a couple coming out.

'*Pardon . . . excusez moi . . .* please forgive me.' Instinctively Monsieur Pamplemousse raised his hat as he stood back to let them pass.

It was a momentary lapse in concentration and he replaced the *chapeau* almost immediately, but the damage was done. Stoniness of expression on the distaff side was tempered by one of triumph as the woman looked him up and down.

'You may not remember,' said Monsieur Pamplemousse weakly, 'but we met in the hotel. I believe you know my brother, Aristide.'

Madame Blanche's wind-dried lips parted reluctantly. 'Indeed I remember meeting you in the hotel. I remember it all too well. But if that is the case, then you are not who you said you were at the time. I suspected as much.'

'I assure you, *Madame . . .*'

'You can assure me until you are blue in the face,' said Madame Blanche, her voice trembling with rage, 'but with my own eyes I have just seen proof positive of your identity. I was right all the time. You are Aristide Pamplemousse. Why you should wish to pretend you are his twin brother I do not know – although I fear the worst.'

Conscious that Madame Blanche had been addressing the

crowd as much as himself, Monsieur Pamplemousse did like-wise.

'It is the penalty one pays, *Madame*, for a moment of madness,' he boomed. 'Now that you have divulged our guilty secret to all and sundry, I only hope my wife is as forgiving as your husband must be, although in her case I feel she will find it harder to understand.'

For a moment he thought she was going to explode.

'Did I hear her say Aristide Pamplemousse?' asked the *gendarme* as Monsieur and Madame Blanche swept down the path and pushed their way through the crowd.

Monsieur Pamplemousse nodded as he followed the other inside.

'Not Aristide Pamplemousse, late of the Paris Sûreté?'

Monsieur Pamplemousse nodded again. 'My twin brother. The poor woman is demented. She keeps mistaking me for him.'

The *gendarme* looked at his charge with new respect. 'He is famous.'

'A very brilliant man,' said Monsieur Pamplemousse. '*Formidable*.'

'*Formidable*, but also flawed would you not say?'

'No,' said Monsieur Pamplemousse. 'I would not say that.'

'If it was the same Aristide Pamplemousse who was dismissed because of that affair with fifty girls at the Folies,' said the *gendarme*, 'there must be something wrong with him.'

'He was not dismissed,' said Monsieur Pamplemousse. 'He took early retirement. And it was not fifty chorus girls, it was only fifteen.'

'*Quinze*.' There was an accompanying whistle. Clearly to anyone stationed in Cap Ferret the number was immaterial. The prospect of being involved with one chorus girl must be fairly remote; fifteen beyond the wildest of dreams.

Glancing back down the road, the *gendarme* jerked his thumb in the direction of Madame Blanche. '*Monsieur* must be a glutton for punishment.'

Monsieur Pamplemousse followed the direction of the man's gaze. It was a tiny consolation that the Blanches seemed to be engaged in a violent argument about something.

'It was a very dark night,' he said.

'Pitch black I should think.'

The *gendarme* led the way past some startled art lovers who were clearly more used to seeing their life studies on canvas rather than face to face, and into a small room at the side of the building.

'I am sorry to have to treat the brother of Monsieur Aristide Pamplemousse like this.' He rewound the film, then opened the back of the Leica and removed the spool. 'But I have some checking-up to do . . . you understand? I shall not be long.'

'He would have done the same,' said Monsieur Pamplemousse gruffly, 'but while you are about it I would like to use the telephone.'

'There is one on the table by the window,' said the *gendarme*. 'I will make the necessary arrangements. I am sure when they hear who you are related to, it will be no problem. In the meantime, I must ask you to wait here.'

Monsieur Pamplemousse grunted. He could hardly do otherwise.

Left to his own devices, he gazed out of the window wondering what to do next. In the circumstances he could hardly ring Doucette. That would really let the cat out of the bag. Questions would be asked. It was Deauville or nothing. He eyed the curtains thoughtfully. They were made of some kind of netting material, but it was better than nothing.

The Director's number seemed to be permanently engaged. When he eventually got through a maid answered.

Monsieur le Directeur was changing for dinner, but she knew he had been trying to reach Monsieur Pamplemousse.

There was another wait, then the Director himself came on the line. For a change his voice came through loud and clear.

'Why are you always so impossible to find, Pamplemousse? I have come to the conclusion that I must insist you carry some kind of bleeper. I have tried the hotel. I have tried every restaurant within twenty kilometres which is listed in *Le Guide*. I have tried the casino. I even telephoned the Police . . . I spoke to some idiot who said he knew your twin brother. I played along with it, of course. I said he must be mistaken because I happen to know your twin brother very well and he is in Italy.'

Monsieur Pamplemousse groaned inwardly. If the Director had been covering up for him he feared the worst. 'Aaah, that is bad news, *Monsieur*.'

'If it is bad news, Pamplemousse, I do not wish to hear it. I have enough bad news of my own. Today has not been a happy day on the track. My horse came in at ten to three.'

Monsieur Pamplemousse couldn't resist it. 'What time was it due in, *Monsieur*?'

There was a momentary silence at the other end of the line.

'Pamplemousse, if that was meant to be a joke, it was in very poor taste. Please be brief. Time is getting on, and . . .'

'I am in a very vulnerable position, *Monsieur*.'

'Come, come, Aristide. You are no more vulnerable than thousands of others who are making telephone calls at this very moment.'

'With respect, *Monsieur*, there is nothing to prevent passers-by seeing into the room . . .'

'Can I get this absolutely clear, Pamplemousse? Are you telling me you have no curtains? What kind of establishment is the Hôtel des Dunes?'

'I am not speaking from the Hôtel des Dunes, *Monsieur* . . . I am in the *Mairie* at Cap Ferret. There are no curtains at the window because I am wearing them. There is an art exhibition and people are coming and going all the time . . .' Even as he spoke a second coach laden with tourists drew up outside. He retreated across the room as far as the phone cord would allow. 'They are made of netting, and . . .'

'Pamplemousse . . .' The Director sounded weary.

'*Oui, Monsieur?*'

'Pamplemousse, it may be a foolish question, but why are you wearing curtains?'

'Because I have no clothes, *Monsieur.*'

'Aah!' The Director gave a long drawn-out sigh of defeat. 'I won't ask any more. But please be brief. My wife and I are getting ready to go out. Chantal is in the bathroom, but she will be with me at any moment. What is it you want? I hope this doesn't mean your car has broken down yet again. It is high time you took advantage of one of the staff vehicles. I will speak to Madame Grante in the morning.'

'*Monsieur*, there has almost certainly been a murder at the Hôtel des Dunes . . . possibly two . . . The chef and his principal assistant . . .'

'The food is that bad?' He had gained the Director's attention at long last. Having gained it, Monsieur Pamplemousse pressed home his advantage.

'I fear there may be worse to come. I am carrying out your instructions to watch over Elsie, but I am somewhat hampered at present. Elsie and I are separated, and until I get another suit and a good lawyer it will remain that way. After your last message I thought you should know that. I cannot in truth say that I am sorry. As far as I am concerned Elsie can stew in the *bouillon* from her own *pot-au-feu*. She is wholly irresponsible. As for her ever becoming an Inspector . . .'

'Pamplemousse . . .'

'*Oui, Monsieur?*'

'This is splendid news. Surely, that is the whole object of the exercise. I knew I could rely on your good offices. All I need from you now is a report to that effect. I fail to see the problem.'

'*Monsieur!* Until I am given some new clothes there will be no report. Not only have I lost almost everything I was standing up in, but I am being held in the *Mairie* at Bélisaire pending charges.'

'Charges, Pamplemousse? What charges? Surely you are not being accused of the murders?'

'No, *Monsieur*, mine are quite minor offences I assure you and I have an answer for all of them . . .'

'Pamplemousse, the reason I tried to contact you earlier was to reassure myself that all is well. Now I regret having spoken to you. Tell me the worst. A moment ago you used the word *charges*. Are you telling me there are more than one?'

Monsieur Pamplemousse did a quick count with his free hand. 'It depends, *Monsieur*, on whether or not they wish to throw the book at me. I am afraid I have run out of fingers.

'Causing a disturbance in a restaurant . . .

'Stealing a dog . . .

'Causing it unnecessary distress by force feeding it with mustard . . .

'Leaving the same restaurant without paying the bill . . .

'Then there was an unfortunate incident with a child. I was merely trying to discover where it had bought its skateboard, but its mother thought otherwise . . . my motives were misunderstood . . .

'Travelling on a vehicle belonging to the *Tramways du Cap Ferret* without the benefit of a ticket . . .

'Disturbing the peace *sur la plage* . . .

'Indecent exposure . . . possibly there will be more than one charge on that count . . . I am afraid that while I was standing on a chair in order to take down the curtains a coach party arrived . . .'

'Pamplemousse!' There was an explosion from the other end of the line. 'I do not wish to hear another word.'

'It is difficult not to expose yourself, *Monsieur*, when the only item of clothing you possess is a *chapeau*. Especially when you wish to avoid being recognised lest someone should by some misfortune link your name with *Le Guide* and telephone one of the less reputable *journaux*. And, of course, it is not just *Le Guide*. There is Elsie to think of, not to mention your own good name, *Monsieur*, and that of your wife. In the circumstances she would not be pleased.'

He knew by the silence which followed his last remark that he had scored a direct hit.

'What is it you require, Aristide? Even at this late hour I will endeavour to pull strings, but it is the very last time. Fortunately it is the height of the season. Deauville is alive with Deputies. This afternoon there were more members of Government to be seen at the race track than there were runners for the whole of the meeting . . .'

'*Monsieur* . . .'

'Yes, Pamplemousse?'

'*Monsieur*, while you are arranging for my release, I wonder if it would be possible to organise a new set of clothes? I take a size thirty-nine collar. Also some shoes and some money. And, *Monsieur* . . .'

'Yes, Pamplemousse?' A note of weariness seemed to have crept into the Director's voice again.

'If you are talking to Madame Grante, perhaps you would be kind enough to tell her I have mislaid my narrow angle lens?'

Monsieur Pamplemousse replaced the receiver. He had a satisfactory feeling he wouldn't have much longer to wait. Soon the telephone lines radiating out from Deauville would start to hum.

Drawing up the only available chair, he placed it with its back towards the window and made himself as comfortable as circumstances allowed. If he kept very still there was always the chance that he might be mistaken for a discarded work of art.

Casting his mind back over the afternoon's events Monsieur Pamplemousse had a sudden thought. He knew there had been something odd about the Blanches. It had been hovering in his subconscious and now he remembered what it was.

Monsieur Blanche had been wearing a leather thong around his neck. Attached to it had been a miniature sextant; an antique model of the kind used by navigators when they wished to take an accurate measurement of the angle between two terrestrial bodies.

Madame Blanche had been carrying a notepad and pencil.

Furthermore, they had both been heading in the direction of the lighthouse.

8
ROBBERY WITH VIOLENCE

If Monsieur Pamplemousse had been born with a tail he would have wagged it unashamedly. The sight of Pommes Frites wagging his own appendage furiously as he drew near the harbour in Bélisaire gave rise to feelings it was impossible to describe.

Ignoring the waiters as he hurried past the waterside café Monsieur Pamplemousse greeted his friend like a long lost brother. The response was satisfyingly mutual.

Pommes Frites was overjoyed. Waiting on the *quai*-side had been his second brainwave of the day. His thinking had been that since they had arrived by boat, it was more than likely his master would go back that way. All the same, he could hardly believe his eyes when he saw Monsieur Pamplemousse coming down the road. Even the fact that he appeared to be wearing a suit which was several sizes too small for him failed to dampen his relief. As for the way he was walking – in a kind of mincing, crab-like motion, as though his feet were hurting – that was neither here nor there. The simple truth was there for all to see. His master was alive and well.

Patently Pommes Frites' line of reasoning more than made up for his earlier débâcle on the beach, but it had taken its toll and he felt quite worn out as they made their way on to the pier. Given a choice between exercising his grey matter and a run along the beach, Pommes Frites would have chosen the latter every time; it was much less tiring.

Ignoring the hunger pains gnawing away at his stomach – he could hardly expect to be welcomed with open arms at the restaurant – Monsieur Pamplemousse led the way along the jetty and joined a small group waiting outside the ticket office for the arrival of the last ferry to Arcachon. Already it could be seen heading their way.

Idling away the remaining few minutes before the boat arrived, he expended two francs of his change on a coin-operated telescope. To his disgust it didn't work. He slapped it several times but nothing happened. The screen remained obstinately blank. The harbour master emerged from his box and struck it once with the palm of his hand. There was a click. The trick wasn't so much how forcefully you hit it as of knowing exactly where to apply the blow.

'You have done it before?'

There was an answering grunt. 'You are the third today.' It sounded as though a fourth customer might be unlucky.

Monsieur Pamplemousse pointed the telescope in the direction of the mainland. Viewed from a distance towards the end of the day the Dune du Pilat had a vaguely menacing air about it. Despite the lateness of the hour there were still people to be seen. Magnified by the lens they appeared as so many ants, rushing hither and thither in an apparently aimless fashion. Lower down he spotted a few motor boats bobbing about in the water near the shore. He wondered if Elsie's was one of them. They might have returned to the hotel that way. He panned up and to the left, but it was impossible to make out anything amongst the trees. He panned down again. The rescue station looked as though it was about to close for the night. He was in the act of following a water skier who shot past when there was a click and the screen went blank. Monsieur Pamplemousse decided not to incur the displeasure of the harbour master by risking another two francs. He wasn't at all sure what he was looking for anyway. Elsie? Hardly. It was too far away to recognise anybody.

Elsie was a problem. It was hard to watch over someone as self-willed as she was.

And yet . . . his gaze softened . . . there was something very beguiling about her: a mixture of being street-wise and yet surprisingly innocent at the same time. It must be her blue eyes. He ought really to give her one more chance. This evening he would insist they get down to writing out a report. In the circumstances they could hardly include the hotel restaurant - or even the hotel itself. They would have to seek out a typical restaurant in the area and concentrate on that. *Le Guide*'s standard form covered every aspect of dining out – nothing was left to chance. All the same, completing it was still a daunting task requiring a good deal of effort. It would be interesting to see what Elsie made of it.

One thing was certain. The chief wouldn't be too pleased if Monsieur Pamplemousse went back on what he'd said over the phone.

Monsieur Pamplemousse was still lost in thought as he clambered on board the ferry. They cast off almost immediately. Pommes Frites took up a position of honour in the bows. With the wind furrowing his brow as they gathered speed he looked for all the world like a carved figurehead, and almost as inscrutable.

Monsieur Pamplemousse bent down to remove his shoes. As he massaged his aching feet he felt a patch of soreness across his back and chest. If he wasn't careful he would suffer for it over the next day or two. It was a long time since he had exposed himself quite so much to the elements.

Getting the shoes back on was a struggle. It took him all the way to Arcachon and the rest of the passengers had already disembarked by the time he and Pommes Frites scrambled on to the steps of the pier. There were still a few fishermen to be seen. It looked as though most of them would be eating out that night. As they reached the end of the line a man standing slightly apart from the rest half turned and caught Monsieur Pamplemousse's eye.

'The chief wants to see you in his office right away.'

Monsieur Pamplemousse hesitated. Then, as the man bent down over his empty basket, he took the hint and went on his way.

'*D'accord.*'

All the same, it was a case of first things first. A visit to a late-night chemist for some sun-burn oil was top priority.

His search took him through the town and along past the parking area in front of the *gare*. To their left most of the cafés and restaurants were already full. It reminded him once again that it was a long time since he had eaten anything. Averting his gaze, Monsieur Pamplemousse glanced across the road and to his surprise he caught sight of Elsie standing by his car. Clearly her mind had been running along parallel lines to Pommes Frites'.

Waiting until there was a gap in the traffic, he crossed over and headed towards her. She was dressed as he had seen her earlier in the day and she was carrying a large oblong-shaped parcel wrapped in brown paper.

He felt a surge of excitement as they drew near and she waved. Resolutions about reading the riot act went out the window.

'Are you alright?' Elsie looked genuinely concerned. 'I was beginning to think the worst.'

'I could say the same about you.'

Contriteness replaced concern. 'Oh, dear. I'm sorry about this morning. It was a case of needs must.'

The translation eluded Monsieur Pamplemousse. 'Did you have a good day in Bélisaire?'

'Not so as you'd notice,' said Elsie. 'Pommes Frites chased us off the beach din 'e? Who's a naughty boy then?'

Pommes Frites looked round, unsure whether he was being addressed or not.

Monsieur Pamplemousse glanced at the parcel. 'But you were able to do some shopping?'

'Yeah.' Elsie's eyes went glazed, as they always did when something came up she didn't wish to discuss.

Having drawn a blank, Monsieur Pamplemousse decided to try another tack. 'Don't you think it is time we had a little talk?'

'I thought you might say that.' If anything, Elsie looked relieved. 'I was hoping you could give me a lift back to the hotel.'

Monsieur Pamplemousse hesitated. He had no wish to incur the displeasure of the officer in charge. And it would mean waiting even longer for dinner. But on the other hand he didn't fancy the thought of taking Elsie along to the *gendarmerie* with him. 'I am afraid that is not possible,' he said. 'I have somewhere else to go before I return.'

'Please.' Elsie snuggled up to him. It was a most disconcerting habit. 'I don't know as I want to go back there alone. Not now most of the others seem to 'ave left.'

Monsieur Pamplemousse wanted to ask what had happened to her American friend. He resisted the temptation.

'All right, we'll go back.' He led the way towards his car.

'I need a change of shoes from my room,' he said gruffly. 'My feet are killing me. We can talk on the way. Pommes

Frites had better stay with you at the hotel. He will make sure you come to no harm.'

Elsie settled herself in the front seat. 'Are you cross with me?'

'Me? Cross?' Monsieur Pamplemousse turned and looked at her as they drove out of the car park and joined the stream of homeward-bound traffic at the roundabout. He used the moment to choose his words with care.

'Perhaps disappointed would be a better word.'

'Don't tell me you're jealous.'

'I have no cause to be jealous.' The words came out with rather more heat than Monsieur Pamplemousse intended. 'It strikes me that you are not being particularly faithful towards your boy friend.'

'Reginald? Oh, 'e'd understand. It was 'is idea. Anyway, 'e can't be here on account of the fact that he's otherwise engaged on 'er Majesty's pleasure.'

'He is with a government department?'

Elsie gave a hollow laugh. 'Dead right. He's doing bird.'

'*Oiseau?*' Monsieur Pamplemousse looked puzzled.

'You know . . . bird-lime . . . time. It's cockney rhyming slang for "in the nick".'

'Oh, dear. I am sorry. That is unfortunate.' Monsieur Pamplemousse wasn't sure what to say. It would certainly put paid to Elsie's chances of getting a job with *Le Guide*. The Director would never countenance employing an Inspector whose credentials or those of their nearest and dearest were not entirely beyond reproach.

'I shouldn't waste any sleep,' said Elsie cheerfully. 'I told 'im that's what comes of being a naughty boy. Besides, 'e knows how to look after number one, does Reginald. He's in what they call an "open" prison. It's ever so nice. You should see 'is cell. It's like an 'otel room. Television. Cocktail cabinet. Fax machine. He reckons it's more cost effective than an office. There are no overheads - 'cept for the odd 'andout here and there. They're a greedy lot of bastards. But apart from not getting his oats as often as 'e would like, he's doing all right. Mind you, it couldn't 'ave 'appened at a worse time. That's why I'm over 'ere.'

'You mean you are doing it for Reginald rather than for yourself?'

'That's right.' Elsie seemed relieved to have got it off her chest.

Monsieur Pamplemousse felt his mind racing as he drew into the hotel car park. It certainly explained why Elsie's mind wasn't on her job.

'But why does Reginald want you to be an Inspector? I thought you said he wasn't interested in food.'

Elsie felt in her bag. 'Look – 'e'd kill me if 'e knew I'd told you, but I'll give you a clue.' Unfolding a newspaper cutting, she handed it to him. It showed two men on sand tractors posing alongside a Sherman tank partly submerged in a sand dune.

'Guess where that picture was taken.'

'Here? In Arcachon?'

Elsie nodded. 'It wasn't on the beach at Brighton.'

Monsieur Pamplemousse glanced at the date. It was the spring of that year.

'It must have happened during the big storms.'

'Right again.'

'So your Reginald is interested in government surplus?' It was a shot in the dark.

'Amongst other things,' said Elsie. 'You could say that Reginald's interested in anything that's surplus. That's why 'e's got where 'e 'as.'

* * *

Monsieur Pamplemousse was still mulling over Elsie's last remark as he finally entered the *gendarmerie* in Arcachon.

The *officier* was standing by the window in his room waiting for him. He glanced pointedly at his watch and then, waving aside Monsieur Pamplemousse's apologies, motioned towards a chair opposite his desk. A lamp was half-angled towards it. It was the classic questioner with his back to the light situation.

It struck Monsieur Pamplemousse as he seated himself that the man looked a little older than when he had last seen him. He judged him to be in his early forties, but he could have been ten years older. Grey hair, close cropped: a face which had already seen better days.

It was tempting to say he knew the feeling. That he, too, in his job often had to work long hours: driving, eating rich meals – when all he wanted to do was get to bed with a glass of wine and a sandwich. But he knew what the response would be. It was almost universal whenever the subject came up. 'I should be so lucky!' The grass was always greener on the other side of the fence.

'Well, Monsieur Pamplemousse . . . late of the Paris Sûreté . . .'

'You know?'

'I'm not sure that I ever thought otherwise, but I was prepared to respect the reasons behind your desire for anonymity. Although in the beginning I was a little unhappy that you might be muscling in on our territory.

'Anyway, it wasn't difficult. Earlier today I had a strange man on the telephone who professed to know your twin brother well. Afterwards, I had only to check with your records.'

Monsieur Pamplemousse could picture it. The Director going out of his way to be circumspect, but at the same time overdoing the embroidery. He would have aroused the suspicions of the girl on the switchboard let alone a police inspector.

'*Alors* . . .' The *officier* accompanied his raised hands with a shrug. 'Let us forget the past,' his gesture said. 'Now to business.'

He went straight in.

'Have you noticed anything odd about the Hôtel des Dunes?'

'Are you asking me in my capacity as an ex-member of the Sûreté?'

'I am asking you as someone probably over-averagely observant.'

'It is bizarre. The whole place is a disaster area. The service is practically non-existent. The food is not fit to be fed to the seagulls . . .'

The *officier* tried another tack.

'What do you know about the last war? More specifically, what do you know about looting?'

Monsieur Pamplemousse felt bewildered. He had expected to be questioned about murder in the recent past, not things that had happened in his childhood.

'I was brought up in the Auvergne and in the beginning it didn't affect us as much as it did those who lived in the big cities. We were part of the unoccupied zone. Those of us who lived there were more concerned with helping our parents look after their few cows and sheep.'

'And the looting of works of art? What do you know of that?'

'On a personal level, very little at all. Mostly it is what I have heard and read since. I know that in many countries it was systematic, ruthless and on a vast scale. Not just private collections, but whole museums – national treasures. Hitler had dreams of establishing a cultural centre in Linz where he was born – it was to be the Mecca of the art world – so vast it would make the Louvre look like a small town museum. The Nazis took into "protective custody" everything they could lay their hands on.'

The *officier* opened a drawer of his desk and removed a bulky manilla folder. He opened it up and laid it out facing away from him.

'Take a look at this.'

Monsieur Pamplemousse skimmed through the first few pages. It was a familiar story. The systematic rape of Europe by Hitler. He had read it all before. It went far beyond the taking of livestock, food, arms, ammunition, rolling stock, ships, copper, zinc, lead, and raw materials of every kind. The entire gold reserves of Czechoslovakia had been annexed; the Hungarian Crown Jewels removed for 'safe keeping'.

The further east the Germans had gone the more ruthless they had become – Hitler had no great regard for their culture; the whole of Poland was plundered in less than six months; churches, museums, private collections, nothing was sacred. Later on it was the turn of Russia. Leningrad was pillaged, then Kiev and Kharkov. Nearer home, France, Holland and finally even their old allies, Italy, had been forced to yield up their treasures. One way and another the Third Reich ended up with the largest single collection of accumulated wealth in the world.

The only good thing about Hitler's ambition was that at least much that might have been destroyed for ever was saved for posterity. In just one mine near his hideaway in Berchtesgaden nearly seven thousand canvases were found; paintings by Fragonard, Watteau, Bellini, Titian, Canaletto, Rubens, Van Dyke. They were worth a fortune then; by today's prices the value would have been astronomical.

Monsieur Pamplemousse leaned back. 'A very thorough review of what went on, I'd say. I must congratulate you.

Clearly, had he won the war, Hitler would have been the possessor of undreamed-of wealth.'

The *officier* rose from his desk and crossed to the window. 'Fortunately he didn't. He lost. And at the end of the war came the total collapse of Germany. During the final weeks when it became clear which way things were going, a great panic set in. Everything had to be shifted, and shifted quickly. Not just the loot, but the entire contents of German museums were packed away in crates in order to keep them safe from the Allied bombers.

'As you may know, the Bavarian salt mines became a favourite destination. In many ways they were ideal; the perfect hiding place. They were nearly always in sparsely populated areas. They had a constant temperature of between 45 and 65 degrees, and most of them contained some kind of rail system which made movement easy. The scale of it all was astronomical. In the Merkers Mine alone there was a hoard with an estimated value at that time of over $300,000,000. Any attempt at keeping a record of what came in soon went by the board. The hills, as they say, were alive to the sound of music, only it was the music of the cash register.

'There it all was – an unbelievable amount of wealth lying about in caves and tunnels – crates of books here, *objets d' art* there, tapestries, Greek sculptures, Egyptian and Roman busts, coins, gold and silver bars; currency – U.S. dollars, Swiss francs, French francs, suits of armour alongside some of the great masterpieces of the world, much of it stolen from the great Jewish family collections whose owners had long-since perished in the gas chambers.'

'So . . .' Monsieur Pamplemousse asked the question he'd been dying to ask ever since the other had begun his dissertation. 'What has all this to do with the murder of an inn-keeper in Arcachon?'

149

The *officier* turned away from the window. 'Very few things in this world are entirely black and white. The Allies had their gangsters too, not to mention just plain opportunists. The American army, who were first on the scene, wasn't just made up of good people. No army ever is. In some areas corruption was rife. Small-time gangsters got big ideas.'

'Things went missing . . . *en route*?' Somewhere at the back of Monsieur Pamplemousse's mind a glimmer of light began to dawn, but he decided to say nothing for the time being.

'There was chaos everywhere. Those who had survived the war were still in a state of shock; dazed and apathetic. The railways had been destroyed. Roads were blocked by refugees pushing prams, carts, bicycles – anything with wheels they could lay their hands on. Cities and towns lay in ruins. In some areas there was a total breakdown in communication, water, power, gas – all the things one normally takes for granted. No one was going to query the movement of trucks for the simple reason they all had their own problems to do with the simple process of staying alive. People would do anything for a carton of cigarettes or a pound of butter. For anyone wanting to make a quick fortune the opportunity was handed to them on a plate.

'It wasn't so much the gold. Gold is one thing – solid bullion is heavy – each ingot weighs anything between 10 and 20 kilograms – it has its problems. Also, it was mostly accounted for, counted and checked, and always – again by its very nature – it was sent under escort. Gold was to do with governments.

'But works of art were something else. Who really knows the true value of a painting? The task of cataloguing it all was monumental. A truck-load of gold bullion has a certain value. Who can say what a truck-load of paintings or other works of art is worth? Imagine being a GI detailed to take a lorry containing untold treasures to some destination you had never even heard of before – just a pin-prick on the map – five or six thousand kilometres away from home.'

Monsieur Pamplemousse broke in. 'You are saying that even now, forty-five years later, there is still a lot that is unaccounted for?'

'Of course. How could it ever be otherwise?'

'So?'

'So.' The *officier* sat down in his chair again and closed his eyes. 'Picture a night in 1945, 20th April to be precise. A lorry draws up outside the Hôtel des Dunes. It is driven by a young lieutenant in the American army. He is accompanied by three other men and his current mistress – a German girl. They ask for accommodation and they are given it. They are free with their cigarettes and their food and they clearly have plenty of money. The owner is only too willing to oblige. They stay at the hotel, mostly sleeping during the day and going out at night. Some days later, when the time comes for them to leave, the lorry is empty. The owner of the hotel – Monsieur Bouet's father – is sworn to secrecy. He hasn't seen a thing. Anyway, what is there to tell? He truly hasn't seen anything. Then they drive off into the night and they are never seen again.'

'Never? Isn't that a little strange?'

'There are a number of possible reasons, but it may simply have been that the authorities made it too hot for them. The U.S. Office of Strategic Services formed an Art Looting Investigation Unit. It was made up of experts in the field and their brief was to track down looted art treasures and return them to their rightful owners as quickly as possible. In a desire to establish good relations with freshly occupied countries it was given top priority.

'A lot of those who on the spur of the moment thought they were on to a good thing quickly discovered that stealing a lorryload of treasure is one thing, reaping the benefit is something else again. Actual cash can be laundered gradually over a period of time without arousing too much suspicion. Works of art have their own problems. How do you get it back home? What do you do with it once it is there? A lot of people must have written the whole thing off as a bad job; a kind of drunken spree which looked totally different in the cold light of day when they eventually sobered up.

'Even back home they weren't safe. The CIA and the FBI started watching bank accounts, looking for any sign of sudden wealth.

'Some people managed to solve the problem, but it didn't do them much good. Here, I will give you an example.' The *officier* leaned forward, reached across the desk and turned over the pages until he came across the one he wanted.

Monsieur Pamplemousse glanced at a press cutting taken from an American *journal*. It was dated 1 July 1990. On one side of the page there was a picture of a tumbledown group of buildings. It was captioned 'The Texas Connection'. Alongside the opposite page someone had attached a translation of the accompanying text.

It had to do with the discovery in some small derelict farm town in Texas – a town of boarded up shops and deserted streets about an hour's drive from Dallas - of a cache of Nazi loot. Investigation showed it had been smuggled back to the States over a long period of time by a former GI whose unit had accidentally stumbled across the hoard in a cave outside Quedlinburg. It had been the subject of an investigation at the time, but that had ceased in 1949 when Quedlinburg became part of East Germany. The extraordinary part of the whole story was that over the years the man had had it sent home through the mail without a single item being queried. The total value was many millions of dollars. The man – respected owner of the local hardware store and an orchid-fancier in his spare time – had died of cancer ten years ago. Steps were being taken to return the property to its original owners.

'Truth,' said the *officier*, 'is often stranger than fiction. I could give you many more examples.'

'And you think something similar may have happened here in Arcachon?'

'Whoever stayed at the hotel didn't drive all that way for the oysters. It must have been because they wanted to bury something in the dunes.'

'But why Arcachon? It is a long way from Bavaria.'

'So much the better. Picture yourself in the same situation. There you are in a strange country: an alien land. You hardly speak the language. You certainly don't trust the natives. After all, for six years you have been at war with them. Suddenly you have the chance to get your hands on untold wealth.'

'The stuff that dreams are made of . . .'

'Dreams, yes – we all have them from time to time. Dreams of winning the *Loterie nationale* perhaps, or being left a fortune. But we are dealing with the harsh practicality of a lorryload of art treasures.

'What do you do with it?'

'Hide it?'

'Yes, but where? Bearing in mind you may not be able to touch it for a long time; certainly not for many months, possibly years, it needs to be somewhere safe.

'Then I know what I would do. I would get the hell out of it. I would drive as far away from the scene as I possibly could. Which is exactly what they must have done.

'Having made their getaway they probably talked it over between themselves. Someone suggests going to Paris. People are naturally more observant in the country; they know all that is going on. A big city would be safe. But no one knows Paris, so that is out. Lyon? Marseille? Nice? They are just names. Time is of the essence.

'They rack their brains. Then someone mentions Arcachon and its dunes. Perhaps they had passed through after the invasion and it stuck in their mind. In many ways it must have sounded ideal. The dunes are not getting any smaller. If anything, they are growing in size. No one is ever likely to build on them. Any tracks they left in the sand would have been obliterated almost immediately. It is safe from the elements . . . all, that is, except one.'

The *officier* reached across and turned to another page.

'They reckoned without the wind.'

Monsieur Pamplemousse recognised the press cutting. It was identical to the one Elsie had been carrying in her handbag. This time he took the trouble to read the caption beneath the picture: 'The hulk of an American-made Sherman tank found on a beach near Arcachon, south-western France. The tank, which had been buried in sand, was uncovered by heavy storms on Wednesday.'

Monsieur Pamplemousse looked up. 'The storms were that bad?'

'The worst ever recorded. Millions of pounds worth of damage was done.'

It was true. Paris had suffered that year. Trees in the Bois de Bologne and the Luxembourg Gardens had been uprooted.

'And you think Monsieur Bouet may have discovered something much more valuable than a tank?'

'I know he did. The first of the pictures began appearing on the walls of his hotel soon afterwards. It was spotted by one of our men when he was making a routine check about another matter. He happened to pass some lighthearted comment about business being good and Monsieur Bouet went into a great panic. Anyway, he carried on about it so much the officer's suspicions were aroused.'

'How about Madame Bouet?'

'She swears he never told her where he found them. He said it was better she didn't know. The fact is that by then, as he began to realise the true nature and value of his find, he was probably almost beginning to wish he hadn't come across it. Like the ones who originally buried them he suddenly didn't know what to do. Again, it was a matter of quantity and of ergonomics. His first instinct was probably ''finders keepers'', but where was he going to keep them?'

'He was probably taking legal advice. Laws on these matters are not as clear cut as one might imagine.'

'They seldom are,' said Monsieur Pamplemousse drily.

'Establishing the rightful ownership could well involve a long and costly legal battle. The laws of each country are different. There are organisations whose sole purpose is to make sure the property is returned to its rightful owners. I think Bouet was biding his time until he got sound advice as to what to do next.'

'In the meantime the walls of the Hotel were beginning to groan under the weight.'

'*Exactement*. We were about to pull him in for questioning when he disappeared. It is my belief that shortly after Bouet began hanging the pictures in his hotel someone must have stayed there – probably quite by chance – but someone who knew about these things. The art world is small. News travels fast.'

Monsieur Pamplemousse suddenly thought of his conversation with Elsie.

'It is a wonder that so far no one has attempted to steal

the paintings,' he said innocently.

'They will. It is only a matter of time. Up to now they have held back for reasons of greed. They believe there must be more where the present ones came from and they don't want to draw attention to the fact. But when they do . . .' he reached under his desk and flicked a switch. An alarm bell rang. 'The pictures are wired.'

Monsieur Pamplemousse sat lost in thought for a moment. 'Why are you telling me all this?'

The question was met with another. 'In your experience, Monsieur Pamplemousse, what is the most important thing to do when you bury something for a long time?'

'First, make sure it is well protected – in a waterproof container of some kind.'

'And then . . .'

'Of equal importance, I would say, is to make absolutely certain you remember where you buried it: not the next day, or the next week, but possibly years later.'

'For that you would need either something very special and immovable to mark the exact spot or a very accurate bearing – preferably more than one – ideally a triangulation.'

'How about the blockhouse nearest to the hotel?'

'That would be useless. It started off at the top of the hill and now it is halfway down.'

'They wouldn't have known that was going to happen.'

The *officier* nodded. 'That is true. But instinct tells me no. You don't go to the trouble of transporting treasure all across France to the Dune du Pilat and end up burying it somewhere obvious like that. It has to be somewhere within the dune itself.'

'Have you tried looking?'

The *officier* gestured towards a cardboard box in the corner of his office. 'I have had men posing as tourists working on it

with metal detectors for several weeks. So far we have un-
earthed two hundred and thirty francs in coins, three cigarette
lighters, two powder compacts, two metal trouser buttons and
a selection of items from a lady's handbag which even you
might find hard to believe. If we keep going we could end up
with the cleanest dune in western France and still be no further on. It is an impossible task.'

'Are there not more sophisticated devices these days? Can
the army not help?'

'It would cause too much comment. Can you imagine what
would happen once the word got out? It would trigger off
another gold rush. The dunes would be swarming with people.'

He had an answer for everything.

'May I ask a question?'

'Of course.'

'You are not telling me all this for nothing.'

'It is my experience, *Monsieur*, that few people in this
world ever do anything for nothing. You are in a position to
help. You are sitting in the hot seat as it were. We would like
more information on those who are staying at the hotel before
we make our next move.'

'There are very few left now,' said Monsieur Pamplemousse.
'The English family have gone, so have the Germans. Now
the restaurant is closed I suspect most of the others may have
departed too. The only ones left apart from myself and my
colleague, are Monsieur and Madame Blanche and the Americans.'

'Precisely! The Americans.'

'You think one of them may be the lieutenant who stayed
at the Hôtel des Dunes all those years ago?'

'No. He is dead. That much we know. We checked back
through the hotel records and got all their names. They were
probably so sure of themselves they didn't bother with false

ones. Besides, everyone was very identity conscious in those days.

'The FBI have been very helpful. The others have all either died of old age or disappeared without trace. However, it is my belief that before he died the lieutenant passed on at least part of his secret, perhaps quite inadvertently when he saw news of the storm. It would have brought back memories.'

Monsieur Pamplemousse looked at the newspaper cutting again. 'I see it has a Reuters' credit – it will have had world-wide circulation.'

The *officier* laid his hands flat on the table. 'Monsieur Pamplemousse, do not lose sight of the fact that this is no longer simply a case of looking for buried treasure. It is also a case of murder. Double murder.'

'Monsieur and Madame Blanche are neighbours of mine in Paris. Madame Blanche may be *une emmerdeuse* – a pain in the arse – but I doubt if she would ever be a party to such things.'

'Exactement.'

'If you suspect the Americans why do you not arrest them?'

'On what charge? If we arrest them on suspicion of murder where does it get us? Other than the fact that Monsieur Bouet disappeared soon after they arrived, we have no proof. At this moment in time we do not even have any bodies. All we have is a photograph showing a part of one.'

It suddenly occurred to Monsieur Pamplemousse that Pommes Frites could be charged with concealing vital evidence; worse still, destroying it! But he dismissed the thought. It would be impossible to prove.

The *officier* clearly felt the same way. After a slight pause he continued. 'We also have a big query against their names from the other side of the Atlantic. A query which says in effect – watch out!

'Other than that we have absolutely nothing against them. Their visas are in order. They pay their bills. They play the casinos – but they are not alone in that. It does not make them criminals.

'Once again, arresting them will only draw attention to the whole affair, and that I wish to avoid for as long as possible.'

'How can I help?'

'We would like more information about your . . . er . . . travelling companion. It seems to me that, yourself excepted of course, she does not always keep good company. I think she is in need of care and protection. It could be that through her association with the Americans she has learned something we do not know. In which case your co-operation would be appreciated . . .'

'That is not possible.' The words came out automatically, before Monsieur Pamplemousse recalled that Elsie had on occasions behaved very oddly.

The *officier* gave a sigh. 'I feared you might say that. It is a pity. It makes my job less pleasant than it might otherwise have been.' He reached across the desk again and turned the pages of the file until he reached the last one.

Monsieur Pamplemousse gave a start. It was a blow-up of a photo taken of him standing by the train earlier in the day; hat over face, watched in amazement by the occupants of the carriage; in colour. The *gendarme* must have been quick off the mark: not half as dozy as he had made himself out to be.

'That would not look good in *Ici Paris*. An unhappy follow-up to your unfortunate affair at the Folies, would you not say?'

'That is blackmail,' said Monsieur Pamplemousse indignantly.

'*Oui.*'

'Blackmail of the very worst kind.'

'*Oui.*'

'People are arrested every day for less.'

'*Oui.*'

'That is very unfair.'

The *officier* allowed himself a smile for the first time. 'Life *is* very unfair at times, Monsieur Pamplemousse.'

'And that is all you have to say?'

'For the moment, *oui*. I am sure we shall meet again.'

Monsieur Pamplemousse rose to his feet. 'One last question. The lieutenant . . . the one who stayed at the hotel all those years ago. When did he die?'

'Just over a month ago.'

'Of natural causes?'

'He was shot through the back of the head by a bullet from a .44 Magnum. A favourite weapon, I believe, of the American Mafia.'

'I think,' said Monsieur Pamplemousse, 'it is time I returned to the Hôtel des Dunes.'

9
A MATTER OF DEGREES

The Hôtel des Dunes was in semi-darkness when Monsieur Pamplemousse arrived back. The dining-room windows were shuttered and a piece of paper bearing the single word FERMÉ was pasted across the glass-fronted menu case. A quick glance around the parking area revealed only three other cars; the Blanches' Renault 25, the Peugeot belonging to the Americans, and a third – a Renault estate which had been there from the beginning and which he guessed must belong to the hotel.

A single light was burning in the entrance hall but there was no sign of Maurice. Monsieur Pamplemousse pressed the *minuterie* button for the landing light.

He paused halfway up the stairs and took a closer look at the painting. It *was* a Sisley. The signature in the bottom right hand corner was unmistakable. He couldn't think how he'd missed it. Somehow the very fact of knowing who it was by gave the work a whole new perspective, which he had to admit ruefully said something about his knowledge of art. It was certainly a picture he could 'live with': one of his main criteria when it came to passing any kind of judgement.

The light went out and he groped his way towards another illuminated switch. Then he made his way up the second flight of stairs and along the corridor to his room.

Elsie was sitting on the end of the bed eating a chocolate-finger sandwich. Pommes Frites lay on the floor at her feet. He jumped up licking his lips guiltily as his master entered the room. His tongue had a noticeably brown tinge to it.

''Ave one,' said Elsie. 'There's plenty more where this came from.'

Monsieur Pamplemousse didn't wait to be asked twice. It was the gastronomic equivalent of a smoker 'rolling his own'. The sandwich prepared, he took a bite from one end and then regarded the phenomenon of bread which never seemed to grow stale. Doubtless it was an acquired taste.

'Madame Blanche was looking for you earlier,' said Elsie. 'She looked quite put out when she found me in your room.'

'Did she see Pommes Frites?'

'I'm afraid so. If you ask me, I think your cover's blown.'

'Irretrievably,' agreed Monsieur Pamplemousse. At least it was Madame Blanche on the warpath and not her husband. 'Why do you think the Blanches were in Cap Ferret?'

'The same reason as everyone else, I suppose,' said Elsie. 'Taking a look at the lighthouse. Or rather, taking a look *from* it.'

'You did that too?' It confirmed his worst suspicions.

'Amongst other things.'

'Isn't it about time you came clean with me? You are not here because you have ambitions to be an Inspector with *Le Guide*, nor are you here for the simple pleasure of being by the sea.'

Elsie grinned. 'That goes for most of us,' she said. 'How about yourself? Don't tell me you're not intrigued too. A little hotel in the back of nowhere suddenly 'as its walls covered in valuable paintings. It's like a bleedin' art gallery.'

'I am here because you are here. I was sent; you came of your own accord, that is the difference.'

'Funny thing, differences,' said Elsie. 'I mean, take a simple thing like a shovel. There it is. It does the same thing the whole world over, dunnit. I mean, you'd think after all this time someone would 'ave come up with a Mark whatever world standard shovel. But, no. In England we have shovels that are flat and 'ave a proper 'andle you can grip. In France you 'ave shovels shaped like a heart on the end of a broom-stick . . .'

'So what are you saying?'

'I'm saying that if you was to look in the boot of some of the cars parked outside I bet you'd find quite a selection. And what do their owners 'ave in common? Well, for a start they didn't none of them come 'ere to build sandcastles.'

'So why are they here?'

'You could say a love of art. Reginald thinks a tank wasn't the only thing what was uncovered by the storms that Wednes-day. He reckons there were a few crates of goodies as well.'

Monsieur Pamplemousse remained silent. It was often the best way of finding out things.

'Reginald 'as been doing a spot of research while 'e's been inside. 'E thinks there must be a link between the storm and the paintings. How they got there in the first place is something else again, but apparently it all goes back to the last war. Some nut-case in the American army who found himself with a lorryload of loot and didn't know what to do with it. Any-way, Reginald discovered that he stayed in this very hotel.'

Monsieur Pamplemousse began to have a new respect for Elsie's boy friend. A force to be reckoned with. It was a pity he was on the wrong side of the fence.

'That is very enterprising of him.'

'Reginald has his methods,' said Elsie. 'And his contacts. Just 'cause 'e's inside doesn't mean to say he can't use them.'

'What put him on to it in the first place?'

'It's a small world,' said Elsie. 'Once the pictures had been spotted the buzz was on. It was a case of who got 'ere first. Reginald was otherwise engaged so I came instead. As it 'appens, so did one or two others.'

'Tell me,' said Monsieur Pamplemousse. 'Who would you put your money on? The Blanches or your American friends?'

'You must be joking,' said Elsie. 'The Blanches couldn't find a dog's doings in a snowdrift. My American friends mean business and they're not going back home until they've found what they came for, that's certain.'

Monsieur Pamplemousse made himself another sandwich. He wondered if they were addictive.

'I've been doing all the talking so far,' said Elsie. 'Now it's your turn. What's the most important thing to remember when you bury something?'

Monsieur Pamplemousse had a distinct feeling of *déjà vu*. 'It is as well to remember where you put it.'

'Right in one.'

'For that you would need some kind of landmark nearby. Or possibly one further away from which you could take a bearing. For safety's sake, preferably the latter.'

Elsie rose and walked to the window. 'Stand on this chair and tell me what you see.'

Monsieur Pamplemousse followed her across the room and did as he was bidden.

'Well?'

'To my right I see lights from houses dotted about here and there around the bay. If I stand on my toes I can just make out some fishing boats. Beyond them I can see the outline of Cap Ferret silhouetted in the moonlight. I see the lighthouse flashing . . .'

'Exactly. It's just clear of the trees. That's why Reginald specially wanted me to 'ave this room. It's the same room what they 'ad at the time.'

Elsie offered Monsieur Pamplemousse a helping hand as he turned away from the window. 'Well, there you are then. It's simple innit. What more could you want?

'Reginald's been living with it for weeks now – eating, sleeping, drinking it. 'E's 'ad a map of the area pasted to 'is wall. The beauty of it is you don't even need a compass. You just go out the back door of the hotel, stand under the window of my room, then walk in an exact straight line towards the light. Somewhere along the route you'll find what you're looking for.'

'I see certain snags to that theory,' said Monsieur Pamplemousse. 'Your path would take you across some five hundred metres of soft sand. It wouldn't be easy to keep to a straight line. Also, you would need to know exactly where to stop. There must be some other measurement we don't know about. However, there is another even more fundamental problem.'

'What's that?' asked Elsie.

'The robbery took place in the spring of 1945. *D'accord?*'

'Yeah. Reginald reckons they got here in April. 20 April to be exact. He 'ad someone check the old register.'

'In that case they wouldn't have seen the lighthouse,' said Monsieur Pamplemousse.

'What do you mean – they wouldn't 'ave seen it? Don't tell me it was blacked out.'

'No. It simply wasn't there. The Germans destroyed it in 1944 – it wasn't rebuilt until 1946.'

Elsie looked at him disbelievingly. 'How do you know that?'

'Fate,' said Monsieur Pamplemousse. 'A combination of somewhat unusual happenings took me to the lighthouse this afternoon and by sheer chance I happened to overhear a conversation someone was having with the guide.'

He almost wished he hadn't told Elsie, she looked so crestfallen as she sat down on the side of the bed.

'I'll tell you something,' she said at last. 'If that's the case, Reginald's not the only one who's got it wrong. There's going to be hell to pay when the others find out, especially now someone's killed the goose that laid the golden egg. Old Monsieur Bouet was the only one who knew exactly where the loot was hidden and with him gone the secret's gone too. So everybody's back where they started. Only worse.'

'You think it was the Americans?' asked Monsieur Pamplemousse.

'Well, I don't know about that. Your guess is as good as mine. But from what I've seen and 'eard I wouldn't put it past any of them. It could be that they tried to force it out of 'im and 'e wouldn't play ball.'

'And his assistant?'

Elsie shrugged. 'Perhaps he came across something 'e shouldn't 'ave done. Or he just 'appened to be in the wrong place at the wrong time.'

'I do not wish to alarm you,' said Monsieur Pamplemousse, 'but if all you have told me is true, it seems to me that you could be in considerable danger yourself.'

'Why do you think I've told you all this?' said Elsie.

'I suggest you don't breathe a word to anyone and that you make sure you lock your door tonight.'

'I've got an even better idea,' said Elsie. 'Why don't I stay 'ere again? I feel sort of vulnerable in my room. Especially 'aving a double bed and all. It's ever so lonely all by yourself in a double bed.'

Monsieur Pamplemousse hesitated.

'Go on – be a sport.' Elsie adopted her little girl lost voice as she pressed herself against him and ran her fingers up the lapel of his jacket. 'I can't think of any good reason why not, can you?'

All too aware of a tingle down the back of his neck,

Monsieur Pamplemousse tried hard to leave his mind a blank. His conscience got the better of him.

'How about Reginald?'

'What the eye don't see the 'eart don't grieve for,' said Elsie.

It was on the tip of Monsieur Pamplemousse's tongue to ask if Reginald need ever know, but Elsie forestalled him.

'And don't say 'e need never know 'cause he would. Reginald always does. Mind you, you're quite right. 'E'd throw a fit. 'E 'ates dog hairs on the sheets.'

'Dog hairs?' Out of the corner of his eye Monsieur Pamplemousse caught sight of Pommes Frites clambering on to the bed. He was wearing his complacent 'you win some, you lose some' look. He turned round twice before settling down plumb in the middle.

'Reginald 'ad one go right up inside his big toe once. Agony it was. It took them ages to get it out. 'E swore never again.

'Night, night, then.' Dismissing Monsieur Pamplemousse, Elsie planted a kiss on his forehead, then reached inside her dress and produced a key. 'See you in the morning.'

The key still felt warm to the touch as Monsieur Pamplemousse let himself into room number eleven. He realised suddenly that he had left everything in with Elsie, but he was too tired to worry. Discarding his clothes on the nearest chair he slipped between the sheets and closed his eyes. Sleep came almost immediately.

How long it lasted he had no idea. All he knew when he woke was that he had been suffering a recurrent nightmare: one that he often experienced during times of extreme stress. It was the torture of '*les trois chocolats*': worse than the fiendish Chinese water treatment, more deadly than the wheel. It always began the same way. He would find himself dining alone at one of France's premier restaurants. Always he chose exactly the same menu – *Le menu gastronomique* – seven courses, a selection from the chef's repertoire, each one more exotic than its predecessor, each accompanied by a different wine. And always, no matter how the meal began, he would end up with the same dessert – *les trois chocolats*. A speciality of the house, it was a concoction of such extravagance and such unadulterated richness, it almost beggared description. Moist, yet firm, three different shades of brown . . . the thick cream . . . the raspberry *coulis* . . . the underlying flavour of *Grand Marnier* . . . eating it was an unforgettable experience. It was like hearing the Beethoven Ninth for the very first time.

L' addition taken care of, he would experience the usual difficulty in rising from the table. His 2CV would be waiting for him at the door. Willing hands would lever him into the driving seat and then, as he emerged from the entrance gates and set off down a long country road, a hand would reach round from behind and hold a pad against his face . . . there would be a whiff of chloroform . . . then darkness. When he came to he would find himself bound hand and foot to a chair, a spotlight directed on his face.

And then it would happen. Men in dark suits – usually masked – would emerge from the shadows and take it in turns to question him; one after the other, faster and faster, at the same time spooning more and more chocolate dessert into his mouth until he found himself crying out for mercy.

Monsieur Pamplemousse sat up in bed and wiped the sweat from his brow with the back of his hand. Somehow the dream had seemed even worse than usual, perhaps because on this occasion his torturers had manifested themselves as the Americans staying in the hotel. He felt for the pillow, but it must have fallen on the floor.

Gradually he became aware that the sound which had woken him came not from his own voice calling out in a dream, but from somewhere in the distance. It was a police siren and it was getting closer all the time.

Switching on the light, Monsieur Pamplemousse jumped out of bed and made a grab for a dressing gown hanging on the back of the door. He hurried along the corridor, pressing the *minuterie* button as he went. Reaching the stairs he peered over the banisters. As he feared, the painting was no longer there.

Hardly pausing in his stride, he made for his own room and knocked on the door. Elsie opened it almost immediately. Dressed in his pyjamas, she suddenly looked surprisingly small and defenceless. It was the first time he had seen her smoking.

'The picture on the stairs is missing.'

'The Sisley? Gone? Now who would have done a thing like that? You can't trust anyone these days.'

Something in her tone of voice stopped Monsieur Pamplemousse in his tracks.

'Look . . . if you know anything about it . . .'

'Me?' Elsie took a drag of her cigarette. Making an almost perfect O with her lips, she blew an equally perfect smoke-ring. They both watched it float away across the room. 'Why should I know anything about it? What a thing to say!'

Monsieur Pamplemousse tried hard to contain his impatience as he heard the sound of a car drawing up on the gravel outside the hotel. It was followed almost immediately by a second, then a third. Doors slammed. 'I'm telling you this for your own good. The pictures are alarmed. The police will be up here at any moment.'

'They'll 'ave to play hunt the thimble then, won't they?' said Elsie. 'I spy with my little eye something beginning with K.'

Monsieur Pamplemousse took a deep breath. Already he could hear footsteps coming up the stairs.

'Well, I suppose it wouldn't be a "K" in your language,' said Elsie, as she stood up to answer a knock on the door. 'I'm not sure what it is really.'

The *officier* took in the scene with the air of one who, though surprised by nothing in this world, left room in his mind for the occasional unexpected twist of its ingredients. He eyed the dressing gown Monsieur Pamplemousse was wearing. It was, to say the least, several sizes too small.

'I take it, *Monsieur*, you have been here all the time?'

Monsieur Pamplemousse hesitated, uncomfortably aware that, as ever, the Blanches were hovering in the background, hanging on his every word. They were both fully dressed. Monsieur Blanche was carrying a spade.

'You should ask Pommes Frites,' said Elsie. ''E could tell you a thing or three.'

'While you are about it, ask him what he is doing staying here under a false name?' Pushing her way to the front, Madame Blanche pointed to Monsieur Pamplemousse.

He glared back at her. '*Madame* . . . you have no proof.'

'Ask him to show us his knees then,' demanded Madame Blanche. 'If he has a mole on his left knee then he's not who he says he is.'

'I've never seen no mole, not on either of 'is knees,' said Elsie. 'Or anywhere else come to that.'

Monsieur Pamplemousse took hold of the two ends of a silken cord around Elsie's dressing gown and undid the knot. 'I will willingly prove you wrong, *Madame*.' It was a last ditch chance.

The *officier* stiffened. Clearly he had other priorities. 'That will not be necessary.'

He turned to the Blanches. 'I must ask you to go to your

room and remain there while we conduct a search of the building.'

Taking advantage of the commotion as the *officier* and his men clattered off down the corridor banging on doors as they went, Pommes Frites emerged from under a blanket and made his way downstairs. He was wearing his pained expression. Sleep was proving difficult. If it wasn't one thing it was another. Elsie had taken up a surprising amount of room. Not only that, but she had been very restless. In and out of bed like a yo-yo. The current goings-on were the last straw. In the circumstances, and in the absence of any orders to the contrary from his master, swopping Monsieur Pamplemousse's bed for the familiar surroundings of his inflatable kennel seemed a sensible move.

It didn't take Pommes Frites long to have second and even third thoughts on the matter. His pained expression gave way to one of puzzlement. No sooner had he settled himself down than he jumped to his feet again. For some reason the floor of his house felt strangely lumpy. He tried changing his position several times, but to no avail. In the end, unable to stand the discomfort a moment longer, he got up and went back outside in order to investigate the matter.

The cause was immediately apparent, although how it came to be under his kennel he had no idea. It certainly hadn't been there earlier in the evening.

Having removed the offending object, Pommes Frites stood for a moment holding it in his jaws, wondering what to do next. He was tempted to dispose of it behind the nearest bush, but being still in a decision-making mode he had another thought. He knew where there were some other objects just like the one that had been causing all the trouble. He might have temporarily mislaid the various bits and pieces belonging to the owner of the hotel and his assistant, but this was a chance to vindicate himself.

Following a built-in navigational system which owed as much to extra-sensory perception as it did to William Gilbert's discovery of magnetic north, Pommes Frites set forth without further delay.

His actions didn't go unnoticed by a *gendarme* who had been left sitting in one of the police cars. Reaching for his walkie-talkie, he opened the door and set off in pursuit. A moment later heads appeared at various windows of the hotel. Other walkie-talkies began to crackle; other figures appeared out of the darkness.

Pommes Frites' course took him towards the dune. Had he, in fact, continued in the same direction across sand and sea, it would have taken him to the very front door of the Semaphore Tower, a kilometre or so to the west of the lighthouse at Cap Ferret, but he didn't in fact go very far. Having reached a point which was exactly two hundred and ten metres from the hotel or, for those who were mathematically inclined but un- willing to trust their memory, ten times his master's room number, he stopped in his tracks and began to dig.

For a few moments sand flew in all directions; at such times Pommes Frites was no respecter of persons. The gen- darmes who were standing a short distance away craning their necks in order to get a better view of what was happening stepped back a pace or two. Then, as heavy breathing gave way to the sound of claws against wood, they moved forward again in a body.

Pommes Frites paused in his labours and glanced round at them.

It really was a most satisfactory way to round off an evening. And if, in the heat of the moment the saliva from his mouth had caused some of the colours on the canvas to run, it was but a moment's work to drop the painting into the hole and cover it with sand before anyone noticed.

'*Merde!*' Hearing the sound of doors slamming, Monsieur Pamplemousse rushed to the bedroom window and was just in time to see the Americans' Peugeot leaving. Seconds later another car took off in pursuit.

'Don't worry.' Elsie joined him just as the tail-lights disappeared through the trees. 'They won't get far. Even if the police don't catch them, there'll be others on the look out. Reginald may 'ave his faults, but 'e's never been into that kind of thing. There's a contract out on them. The underworld don't like innocent people being killed. They 'ave their code the same as anyone else.'

Monsieur Pamplemousse eyed her curiously as he absorbed the information, trying for a moment to reconcile the matter-of-fact way in which it had been conveyed with the Elsie he had come to know.

'All the same, forgive me, I must get dressed.'

'Before you look inside the wardrobe,' said Elsie, 'I think I should tell you – there's something in there . . .'

'Something?' He paused with his hand on the doorhandle.

Elsie took another drag on her cigarette. 'You'll see.'

'*Sacre bleu!*' Monsieur Pamplemousse stepped back a pace and gazed at a picture propped up against the back wall. It had an all too familiar look about it.

'Nice innit,' said Elsie. 'Told you it would be a surprise. I 'ope you don't mind me putting it there but it's the one place in the 'otel where no one's liable to look for it, you being who you are and all.

'Besides, there's no point in going home empty-'anded. Reginald wouldn't think much of that. He's very keen on Sisley, is Reginald.'

10
WASH DAY

'I must go to the launderette after dinner,' said Madame Pamplemousse.

'Oh, dear, must you, Couscous? Can't it wait until tomorrow?'

'You won't have a thing to wear if I don't. I can't think what you've been up to. Your clothes are in a terrible state.'

'It was the dunes,' said Monsieur Pamplemousse.

He buried himself in his newspaper. The news from Arcachon occupied several columns. Two people were helping the police with their inquiries. One had been charged with carrying an offensive weapon. There was no more to report on either Monsieur Bouet or his assistant. Nor, according to the special correspondent on the spot, was there likely to be for some time to come. The police had an impossible task. It was worse than looking for a needle in a haystack. There was nothing about Elsie. No mention of airports being watched. Most of the story was devoted to the police discovery of the loot and its legal ramifications.

'Anyway,' said Madame Pamplemousse, 'it's a chance to catch up on the gossip. Not that I ever listen to it.'

'No one ever does,' said Monsieur Pamplemousse vaguely. 'But everyone likes it all the same.'

'I want to hear the latest on the Blanches. It seems they're being held for questioning.'

Monsieur Pamplemousse pricked up his ears. 'The Blanches? Do I know them?' he asked innocently.

'You must do. He has a gallery and he writes about art for one of the *journaux*. I see his wife in the launderette sometimes. Apparently Monsieur Blanche was caught carrying an offensive weapon. Nobody knows what Madame Blanche is being held for.'

Monsieur Pamplemousse could guess. Trying the patience of an *officier* for a start. Something must have snapped.

'Funnily enough, Monsieur Blanche has a mole on his left knee just like yours.'

Monsieur Pamplemousse lowered the *journal* and stared at his wife. 'Do you mean to say you have been discussing my mole in a launderette? Is there nothing sacred?'

'People let their hair down in launderettes,' said Doucette. 'You find out all sorts of things. You would be surprised.'

After the latest revelation, Monsieur Pamplemousse had a feeling nothing would surprise him ever again. It gave truth to the old phrase about washing one's dirty linen in public. For all he knew the whole building was aware of his impediments. It was bad enough having the details entered on his P63, his personal detail file, back at *Le Guide's* headquarters.

Any further conversation was interrupted by the telephone ringing. Madame Pamplemousse picked up the receiver.

'It is from Arcachon.'

Monsieur Pamplemousse gave a grunt. He'd been expecting the call ever since his arrival back in Paris. Recognising the signs, Madame Pamplemousse disappeared into the kitchen.

The *officier* went straight into the attack.

'I take it I am talking to the real Monsieur Aristide Pamplemousse and not his twin brother?'

'You have a choice,' said Monsieur Pamplemousse, in an attempt to break the ice. He waited for an answering chuckle, but none was forthcoming.

'We have made an inventory of the pictures.'

It wasn't hard to guess what was coming next. 'There were a large number still in their original crates. A Cézanne, a minor Botticelli, a Seurat, a Fragonard or two. Together with those in the hotel they came to a total of seventy-five. Then there were a great many items in silver and bronze, statuettes and other bits and pieces. I won't bore you with all the details. A full list will be published in due course, along with the total value.

'However, there was one oddity – a painting – measuring some fifty centimetres by thirty. It was more recent than the others and it bore the name of a local artist.'

'It is a small world,' said Monsieur Pamplemousse.

'It was purchased at an art exhibition being held at the *Mairie* in Bélisaire. It depicts a scene not dissimilar to the one by Sisley which was stolen from the hotel. Would you know anything about that?'

'*Non*,' said Monsieur Pamplemousse. 'Definitely and most assuredly, *non*. I can say with my hand on my heart that I have never seen such a painting.'

'My understanding is that it was purchased by an English girl, answering to the description of your companion. She was most insistent that she be given a receipt describing the scene in detail; a canal in summer time. She said it was in case she was stopped at the airport.'

'It sounds like a sensible precaution,' said Monsieur Pamplemousse.

'The paint had run and there were teeth marks on the frame.'

'Perhaps,' said Monsieur Pamplemousse, 'she should ask for her money back.'

'That is all you have to say?'

'I am sorry, but it is a very bad line. Either that, or I have an attack of my old complaint – temporary loss of hearing.'

'Considering I stood up for you with Madame Blanche, I think that is very unfair. I have just let her go, but only under pain of being instantly rearrested should she so much as breathe a word.'

'Life *is* very unfair at times,' said Monsieur Pamplemousse. 'But at least Pommes Frites found the buried treasure for you. In return I would like to keep my self respect.' There was a long silence.

'That is your final answer?'

'*Oui.*'

There was a click and the line went dead.

'*Dîner* is ready,' called Madame Pamplemousse from the kitchen. 'We have *filets de hareng marinés* and *poulet rôti.*'

The herrings came in a large tureen along with sliced carrots, thinly sliced onion and herbs. The accompanying potatoes, quartered, tossed with *vinaigrette*, olive oil and parsley and still slightly warm, were in a separate bowl.

Monsieur Pamplemousse poured two glasses of a lightly chilled Pouilly Fumé Les Charmes, and then took the precaution of removing his tie before he sat down.

'Who was that on the telephone?' asked Madame Pamplemousse.

'It was someone from the *gendarmerie* in Arcachon. One of the *officiers.*'

'You sounded very brusque, Aristide.'

'Not brusque,' said Monsieur Pamplemousse. 'I was merely being firm. He wanted some information which I was not prepared to give.'

They ate in silence for a while.

'Was it nice in Arcachon?' asked Madame Pamplemousse suddenly.

'Very,' said Monsieur Pamplemousse. 'You would like it. It is not too grand.'

'And the hotel? Was the hotel nice?'

'There was a lot to be desired.'

'I have never been to that part of France. Perhaps we could take a holiday there later in the year. When the crowds have gone.'

'I think we should leave it until next year,' said Monsieur Pamplemousse. 'People will be flocking to the Dune du Pilat all through the summer.' He also had no wish to meet up with the *officier* again until the dust had settled.

He wiped the plate clean with his bread. 'That was delicious, Couscous. The herrings were exactly as they should be – not too salty.'

'I took the precaution of soaking them in milk for several hours first,' said Doucette. 'They have been marinating in oil ever since you went away so the onions and carrots have had time to soften.'

While she was preparing the second course, Monsieur Pamplemousse picked up the telephone and dialled the Director's number in Deauville. It was answered on the first ring.

'*Monsieur . . .*'

'Pamplemousse! What news? I have been trying your hotel all day. The number seems to be permanently engaged.'

It was hardly surprising. The Hôtel des Dunes was probably swarming with officials, not to mention the media, all of them wanting to use the telephone. He pitied the poor television cameramen lugging their equipment up and down the dune; worrying about getting sand in their lenses.

179

'I thought you would like to know, *Monsieur*, that you may put your ballpoint away.'

'My *ballpoint*, Pamplemousse? What on earth are you talking about?'

Monsieur Pamplemousse suppressed a sigh. Sometimes he wondered if his chief was being deliberately obtuse.

'The operation, *Monsieur*,' he hissed. 'My reason for being in Arcachon. It has reached a satisfactory conclusion.'

'You mean?'

'Elsie is returning to base. With luck she may already be there. She has given up all thoughts of becoming an Inspector. I doubt if she will need to work again for a while.'

'Aristide, what can I say? I cannot begin to tell you how much I have been through these last few days. I seem to have spent most of my time hiding beneath the duvet. Time has hung heavy.'

'I, too, have suffered, *Monsieur*. And I, too, have returned to base. I am speaking from Paris.'

'Paris? How extraordinary. Doubtless you have seen the news about Arcachon. It is on all the channels. There is no escape from it. How strange that it should all have blown up the moment you leave. You have missed all the excitement.'

'*C'est la vie, Monsieur*. That is life!'

The roast chicken came garnished with watercress. Monsieur Pamplemousse dissected it quickly and expertly. Then Madame Pamplemousse put the legs back in the oven for himself and Pommes Frites later. It was what she called 'the men's portion'. While she was gone he took a quick nibble. It was what he called 'carver's privilege'. The flesh was done to a turn, the skin golden brown. The watercress leaves added a pungent taste.

He went to his wine cupboard in the hall and took out a

bottle of '85 Faiveley Morey St.-Denis Clos des Ormes which he had been saving for a special occasion. Only 95 cases had been made.

'You are spoiling me, Couscous,' he said, as Doucette returned carrying a bowl of green salad and a plate piled high with frites. 'It is a meal fit for a king. I swear the *poulet* would not disgrace L'Ami Louis.'

Madame Pamplemousse looked pleased. 'The trick is in rubbing it first with goose fat, then seasoning it with salt. That is how they do it.'

Monsieur Pamplemousse poured the wine. 'You should have been an Inspector.'

'I haven't lived with one all these years without learning a few secrets,' said Doucette. 'I hope it makes up for all the bad food you had in the hotel.'

Monsieur Pamplemousse looked up in surprise. 'How did you know that?'

'The Director's wife was telling me.'

'Aah! Chantal. Did she tell you anything else?' In case the news was bad, Monsieur Pamplemousse took the precaution of filling his mouth with food so that if he were to be questioned he would have a little breathing space. He immediately regretted it.

'She told me about Elsie. It was such a pity the poor girl struck unlucky on her first time out. It must have put her off any thoughts of becoming an Inspector.'

'Elsie?' Monsieur Pamplemousse emitted a choking noise.

'Such a nice girl, and such a good cook. I think she is really very shy. I'm so glad it was she you had to take and not a lot of people I know. Although I must say I wouldn't have recognised her from the photograph you showed me the other night after the Director's party. Where you got it from I don't know.

'Chantal told me about all the telephone calls. It happened every time she went into the bathroom. She had to wait in there for ages some evenings. Why there had to be such secrecy I really can't imagine.'

'Perhaps,' said Monsieur Pamplemousse discreetly, '*Monsieur le Directeur* was worried on my behalf. He thought you might be jealous.'

'Men! You are such vain creatures. You think that every pretty girl is just waiting for the chance to jump into bed with you. I knew you would be safe with Elsie. It's the unlikely ones you have to watch. People like Madame Blanche.'

'Couscous! How can you say such things?'

'Because I know men. And I know Madame Blanche. I think she rather fancies you on the quiet.'

Not for the first time, Monsieur Pamplemousse reflected that there was no knowing women. But that, of course, was their attraction.

He lifted his glass. 'Here's to things past.'

The wine was smooth and full bodied; an explosive mixture of ripe fruit, with a promise of even greater things to come. Mentally he added a second toast; to Elsie – wherever she might be.

'The past is like a foreign country,' said Doucette, 'where they speak a different language.'

Monsieur Pamplemousse digested the observation for a moment or two. 'That is true,' he said at last. 'It was certainly very true of Elsie.'

Taking another sip of the wine he caught Pommes Frites' eye. Pommes Frites was wearing one of his enigmatic expressions. It was hard to say whether he was registering agreement about Elsie, or whether he was simply waiting for his chicken leg to arrive.

If it were the former, reflected Monsieur Pamplemousse,

then Pommes Frites had the advantage over a great many people. At least he and Elsie had got to share the same bed. He hoped Reginald didn't ever get to know. He might be tempted to put out another contract.

MICHAEL BOND

MONSIEUR PAMPLEMOUSSE

'The Gallic welcome of a kiss on both cheeks for a new detective' *Good Housekeeping*

Monsieur Pamplemousse, inspector of food and detective *extraordinaire*, is delighted to have the chance to dine once more at the famed La Langoustine, a restaurant nestling in the hills of Provence. Life as an undercover researcher for a top-class culinary guide can be lonely, and Monsieur Pamplemousse is ever grateful for the companionship of his friend and helper, Pommes Frites, a bloodhound with a finely-tuned nose.

Will La Langoustine win the longed-for jewel in a chef's crown, a third Red Stockpot? The signs are promising as Monsieur Pamplemousse and Pommes Frites await the delicacy of the house, chicken wrapped in a pig's bladder and stuffed with truffles and foie gras, and the room is filled with a mouth-watering aroma of herbs, wine and spices. As Monsieur Pamplemousse stands to make his first cut with a characteristically deft movement, the outer casing collapses to reveal not the expected treat but a dish of far more grisly proportions. Clearly someone wants Monsieur Pamplemousse out of the way, but nothing delights the detective more than the chance to practise the skills he learnt in his sleuthing days at the Sûreté . . .

'A delightful French frolic of a detective story'
The Scotsman

'An interesting, entertaining and, best of all, amusing romp for the young at heart'
Books and Bookmen

FICTION/CRIME   0 7472 3313 6

MICHAEL BOND

MONSIEUR PAMPLEMOUSSE
TAKES THE CURE

'Chuckles guaranteed' *Sunday Mirror*

When France's leading gastronomic guidebook decides to launch itself into the expanding health farm market, its Director decides Monsieur Pamplemousse is the man for the job: overweight, underactive, with a blood pressure count that threatens to shoot off the top of the scale.

So the former Sûreté detective finds himself banished to the punitive regime of the Château Morgue, a Pyrenean health clinic from which a number of damning reports have already emerged, centred largely on its shady-sounding owner, Herr Schmuck.

The Château Morgue fulfils Pamplemousse's grimmest expectations; obligatory dawn snow tramps, rock-hard beds and meals comprised solely of muddy spa water. And it also provokes his deepest suspicions. Why does a hearse pay such frequent visits? What is going on in the astoundingly luxurious Tower Block? And what is the significance of the delicious parcel of sausages sniffed out by Pamplemousse's indispensable bloodhound, Pommes Frites? With Pamplemousse and Pommes Frites on the trail truth is finally revealed – but not before their sleuthing stamina has been tested to its absolute limits . . .

'Over-the-top fun' *The Times*

FICTION/HUMOUR   0 7472 3328 4

A selection of bestsellers from Headline